Meantime

Meantime:

LOOKING FORWARD TO THE MILLENNIUM

Introduced by Janice Galloway

Polygon

EDINBURGH

In Association with Women 2000

First published in 1991 by Polygon, 22 George Square, Edinburgh

Individual contributions © the Contributors 1991
Introduction © Janice Galloway

Extracts from *Among You Taking Notes:*
The Wartime Diaries of Naomi Mitchison 1939–45,
ed. Dorothy Sheridan (1985), reproduced here
with kind permission from Gollancz

Extract from 'Scotland The Brave – And Me' from
Scottish International Review (1968)

Typeset by Koinonia Ltd, Bury

Printed in Great Britain by Billing and Sons, Worcester

British Library Cataloguing in Publication Data
Meantime: looking forward to the millennium.
  I. Women 2000
  828.91409

  ISBN 0 7486 6093 3

Set in Linotron 11 on 13pt Sabon

Contents

Introduction

Janice Galloway

She didn't write it. *But if it's clear she
did the deed* She
wrote it but she shouldn't have.
*It's political, sexual,
masculine, feminist* She wrote it, but look
what she wrote about *The bedroom, the kitchen,
her family, Other women!*
She wrote it, but only
one of it. *'Jane Eyre. Poor dear,
That's all she ever ... '* She wrote it,
but she isn't really an artist and
it isn't really art. *It's a thriller, a romance,
a children's book. It's sci-fi!*
She wrote it, but she had help.
*Robert Browning, Branwell Brontë.
Her own 'masculine' side.* She wrote it,
but she's an anomaly. *Woolf. With Leonard's
help ...*
She wrote it BUT

(from *How to Suppress Women's Writing*
by Joanna Russ, Women's Press 1984)

The classic cover of Joanna Russ' *How to Suppress Women's
Writing* made witty shorthand of traditional qualifications

that hedged women's writing. Under that cover, more and in more detail; things we'd known a long time in our bones but had never seen so consistently and unapologetically arranged in one body of evidence. The drift of argument was clear, corroborated, irrefutable. It didn't matter how well women wrote: if the writing didn't conform to male standards as to what was 'good' or 'art' or 'worthwhile', it would be judged bad, weak or inferior and would not enter the canon, that 'recognised' body of work which is 'understood' to be 'significant' in literary terms.

That book's evidence, and that of many more since, made it clear the rules for acceptance into the canon are slanted, based on male values masquerading as objective truths. It made clear that the canon, far from being some objective standard, was, as it sounded, a weapon of status quo politics. Between the lines, the message from the existing canon to the woman writer is not encouraging. Even if you do write, and write well, it will be in a 'limited sphere'. Persist at your own risk and don't say you weren't warned. Write in the knowledge it's probably a waste of time because you are inadequate. Write without role models or history for inspiration. Write without encouragement. And expect to fail.

The solution was simple and revolutionary. Ignore the canon. Don't try to enter it because it has been designed to keep you out. It made sense to rediscover Virginia Woolf's insight that

when a woman comes to write a novel, she will find that she is perpetually wishing to alter the established values – to make serious what appears insignificant to a man, and trivial what is to him important. And for that, of course, she will be criticized; for the critic of the opposite sex will be genuinely puzzled and surprised by an attempt to alter the current scale

of values and will see it not merely as a difference of view, but a view that is weak, or trivial, or sentimental, because it differs from his own
and take it to heart by rejigging the popular maxim: if you can't join them, realise they're not as relevant as they think. Fresh standards, fresh approaches: sources of inspiration, ideas, redefinition were the only logical way forward. Women's collections, the logical outgrowth. Then, it was all so obvious.

But.
That was in 1984.
It might be germane to ask what this material is doing as part of the introduction to a book in this day and age. Someplace off to the left, it comes again. The low rustle of post-feminist embarrassment – that line of thinking which claims we know all this stuff now. The process has worked through, it insists, pointing to greater numbers of women appearing in publisher's lists, even more offering work for publication and seeing their work bear fruit. It takes a pride in at least three flourishing women's presses and, thanks to Virago Classics, all those role models coming out of the woodwork like worms after a cloudburst. The balls, so to speak, are in our court. It claims the world is changed and we're all equal now. All equal now.

OH NO WE'RE NOT.

In 1911 there were 21 regular feminist journals and magazines in Britain. There were feminist bookshops, presses and a bank specifically run for women by women. How did something that established just fade out and not leave its mark, so that the feminist movement of the sixties seemed a thing newly conceived? Because female role models are still getting rubbed out, that's why. History writers and canon-makers are still largely people not sympathetic to female perspectives, thus the erosion of female history, female ante-cedents, female achievement and the bases for further devel-opment. To recall Catherine Stimpson's phrase, every fifty years or so, women have to reinvent the wheel.

Bearing this in mind, it seems premature to regard the increasing numbers of women in print and re-editions of classics – without asking the searching questions about just why it was so many books by women fell 'out of fashion' and 'out of print' in the first place – as evidence of change. Change, according to my therapist, is not change at all if it is not deep or lasting; if it does not directly alter old, damaging value systems. And while differences have indeed been ef-fected with regard to confidence, feasibility, acceptance and opportunity for women writers, it doesn't follow that every-thing is swimming.

I had a goldfish once. He was cooped up in a bowl all his life and one day, not surprisingly, he got sick. He flopped over onto his back and started to sink. To all appearances he was dead. Then my mother had this idea to put a tot of whisky in the water. It was the right thing to do because it was the only thing she could think of to do. And it effected a difference. He trembled, flipped round the right way and looped over a couple of times, revved sideways in eccentric circles then swam off, revived. The revival went so well he swam about all afternoon and into the evening. Next morning, he was downside up and dead. Dead as a dout in the gutter. The revival had been good while it lasted. But nothing funda-mental or lasting had occurred. The whisky hadn't changed him into something thriving at all. The whisky was an artificial boost. That's all. That's all. And even if it had worked more lastingly, he'd still have been confined, not free in open water.

That kind of surprise isn't going to get me twice if I can help it. The suggestion we can relegate feminism to the history books because we've all got the same chances and only have to grasp them is so much childlike overeagerness for it all to be OK now. There is no real reason to think the present wave of interest in women's writing will not be allowed to go 'out of print' like the forerunners; no evidence to suggest this present honeymoon with publishers won't pass abruptly when women's writing stops being flavour of the month and there's a less immediate way to make money out of it.

What those lists reflect is an acknowledgement of an exploitable market out there, not a profound ethical shift. Packets of washing powder with GREEN on the front don't mean the ozone layer is back in full working order. It is facile to think things are better so they're fixed. Better doesn't mean fixed. It hasn't even got the same number of letters. We might well have come a long way but the road stretches for an appreciable distance yet. And, of course, there's the matter of where our particular road is.

Scotland.
Scottish women have their own particular complications with writing and definition, complications which derive from the general problems of being a colonised nation. Then, that wee touch extra. Their sex. There is coping with that guilt of taking time off the concerns of national politics to get concerned with the sexual sort: that creeping fear it's somehow self-indulgent to be more concerned for one's womanness

instead of one's Scottishness, one's working class heritage or whatever. Guilt here comes strong from the notion we're not backing up our menfolk and their 'real' concerns. Female concerns, like meat on mother's plate, are extras after the man and the weans have been served. A particularly Scottish set of strangling caricatures make it hard to escape such guilt – from Maw Broon or one of the McIlvanney parade of miracle workers, silent sufferers and mystical creatures with tides and moons, brave nurturers all – they serve exactly the same message as the one served up from the general establishment's canon all these years. Nurture or be deviant and sorry. Pursue your own goals only if you acknowledge it as selfishness. (Non-nurturers are sex-starved old women or morally reprehensible – literal or metaphorical tarts.) So, on top of working out how to write (which is hard enough), on top of the need to reinvent the wheel, on top of finding time, there's the guilt, the guilt. Always the guilt.

Do we need encouragement and the support of other women's writing?

Do you really need to ask?

Yet, all too often, reactions in this country to such unexceptionable things as women's collections are unsympathetic. Among the more believable and common I have heard (and I do mean literally) are:

1. They're for women anyway, these books (as if women readers were a kind of subspecies and not real readers at all);

2. The writing is often substandard which is hardly surprising when these kinds of publications refuse to employ the traditional methods of analysis and criticism (ie the kind invented by men that keep out the genres and issues women might want to explore); or, more paranoically,

3. Anything all-women is, by definition, anti-men (also known as the haven't-these-bloody-women-got-enough-advantages-in-life-already stance); and finally

4. Isn't-it-time-yous-girls-took-your-chances-with-the-Big Boys.

The need to keep women feeling guilty goes deep, obviously. The fear of losing the unfair system that operates in male favour likewise. It is still something for women to bear in mind, something to consciously resist. As is the guilt it hopes to produce. Fortunately, Scottish women writers seem to be finding means of resistance. They're writing.

I hope you find some of that resistance material in this book. It includes selected pieces from a writing competition organised by Ann Karkalas for Women 2000 (a voluntary organization of women interested in creating a higher profile and encouragement for women in the Arts in Scotland in the nineties. For more information on Women 2000, contact Barbara Littlewood at the Department of Sociology, University of Glasgow) and a selection of pieces from well-known women in the public eye: Rowena Arshad, Kay Carmichael, Kathleen Jamie, Liz Lochhead, Ronnie McDonald, Naomi Mitchison, Myrtle Simpson, Anne Smith and the late Joan Ure. We wanted a hybrid, full of vigour enough not to bother about whether pieces conformed or not to recognisable patterns. The competition part was intended to bring in pieces from as wide a cross section of women as possible via newspaper invitation. The competition brief, requesting reflections of hopes, fears, resolutions for the coming decade in any genre, was one we hoped would pool a broad response. Sponsorship from *Scotland on Sunday* (who also provided awards for six commended pieces), an offer of publication from Peter Kravitz of Polygon, and some sifting of submissions by Elspeth Davie, Trevor Royle, Marion Sinclair (for Polygon) and me (for Women 2000) put together the result.

Many of the writers appear for the first time in print. Others have a fair track record of publication behind them. That mix is, in itself, a positive thing. For both writers and readers, there's a chance to see whether any common strands of thought in prose, poetry, non-fiction and fiction writing emerge; a chance to see vastly different pieces in conjunction with each other and enjoy what randomly emerges from proximity, difference, similarity. Simply, the excitement of embracing strange bedbuddies. And, of course, the excitement of other women's ideas. Of their writing.

How much it takes to become a writer. Bent (far more common than we assume), circumstances, time, development of craft – but beyond that: how much conviction as to the importance of what one has to say, one's right to say it. And the will, the measureless store of belief in oneself to be able to come to, cleave to, find the form for one's own life comprehensions. Difficult for any male not born into a class that breeds such confidence. Almost impossible for a girl, a woman.

It might well be the nineties but what little advance has been made with what Tillie Olsen describes here is neither stable nor something to get complacent about. Awareness of the extent of the difficulties is the only way to begin an approach to overcoming them. Of finding sense of the elusive right to say. For whatever reason, I hope you enjoy the book.

And what do *I* see in store for women in the nineties? More of the same, girls. More of the same.

Alternative Vision

Rowena Arshad

To predict the prospects for black* women in Scotland towards the next millennium, we must first look back to the obstacles and achievements faced in preceding decades. Several other questions spring to mind – What do we mean by black women? Where do they fit in the political, social, economic and cultural jigsaw of Scotland? How does racism affect the life chances of black women?

It would be impossible for me to write of black women as of sharing one experience and aspiration. As there are layers of differences within the white women's movement, the same applies to us. That is a crucial point to remember and consider in any debate of the future of Scottish black women.

In looking forward, there is also a need to look beyond what is traditionally stereotyped. For example the commonly perceived pictures of Asian domesticity, oppressed Muslim women, the rural African often from starving nations and so forth. It often comes as a surprise that not all Asian women have arranged marriages nor do they all work in take-aways or corner shops. It is not often thought that young Muslim and Sikh girls, like their white counterparts, participate in outdoor educational pursuits, enjoying ornithology, abseiling

---

*Black - I have chosen the word 'black' to refer to all women of colour who are discriminated against by racist structures and attitudes within Scotland's white-dominated culture.

and hill-walking. Too often for us, it is only our colour that is seen and not all the other dimensions that make up the whole person. It therefore must be remembered that there are elderly black women, black women with disabilities, black gay women, single parents ... The absence of the obvious, eg. a Scottish Black Lesbians Group does not automatically mean there are no black lesbians in Scotland.

In the same way as we have to see the whole woman, we have to understand the term 'black'. Who do we mean when we say 'black' or 'ethnic minority'? Whilst a high percentage of black women in Scotland owe their origins to the Indian sub-continent, others do not. They come from Kenya, Malaysia, Hong Kong, Cameroon, Korea, Chile, Palestine ... Many are born here! There are many community languages spoken apart from Gaelic, Punjabi and Urdu, eg. Cantonese, Swahili, Arabic, Malay, Spanish. Within the Scottish context, the terms 'black' or 'ethnic minority' are often equated to people of Asian descent and at that only people from the Indian sub-continent. If all black women are to enter the next decade with equal rights then it is time this cultural blindness ceases. Women from other parts of Asia, of African and Caribbean descent, from the Middle East must not be trivialised or forgotten. Their heritage, rights, needs and interests should have equal significance. After all, they too have made contributions to the processes of giving voice to our collective experiences as women. Yet policy makers, the media and other institutions do forget these women, hence contributing to further divisions and marginalisation of some black women. This process of divide and rule has long been in existence especially in Asia, Africa and the West Indies where the interests of one group have been catered for and allowed to advance at the expense of others. The women's movement, both black and white, has a duty to prevent this form of divide and rule to continue in Scotland today!

Not Just A Question Of Visibility

Indeed if visibility was the key then the problem of being forgotten or oppressed would cease to exist. Black women have been the subjects of novels, films, musicals, grant-applications for years. We have been in vogue! It is too easy to be deluded by the presence of famous black women, eg. Maya Angelou, Ella Fitzgerald, Winnie Mandela and the like to make it look as if black women were at last emerging from the pits of subjugation. We must remember that these women became visible and strong with much pain. They have combined their talents with protest messages which have often led them away from plush white settings to confrontational black rallies not compromising on their colour or gender.

Some of you reading this might feel people like me have little to complain about. After all, I have been given space in this book to make my contribution and be heard! However, how many black women's life chances follow this path? Yet, one of the reasons I am visible is because it makes the establishment feel better that I am around and seen. I can be the token black – a gap filler! The person who 'balances' the numbers and lends credibility to the game – a conscience salve! The challenge for women like me is not to conform but to challenge the status quo and open doors for many others who remain unheard, unseen and undervalued.

Black women in Britain/Scotland with organisations like OWAAD (Organisation of Women of Asian and African Descent) and the Scottish Black Women's Group have attempted to do this by seeing past the point of divisions to an understanding that in a white and male dominated nation, no matter where you come from, if you are not white, you are going to have to deal with racism and if you are a woman, you will have to deal with sexism. Networking and campaigning together have been their main strengths.

As long as my prospects are seen solely as a result of my religion, culture, ethnic pattern and history then I will continue to be visible only in areas and guises acceptable to a society currently operating within a discriminatory framework.

Equal Opportunities and All That!

Over the last decade, terms like 'equal opportunities', 'anti-racism' and 'multiculturalism' have become buzz words for policy-makers and workers in the statutory, voluntary sectors and industry. On closer examination these have remained paper policies without resulting in any radical changes, merely a tinkering at the edges. A recent study by Gibbon in 1989 argued that rather than increase opportunities for black people and women, these policies have on the whole had the effect of enhancing the employment prospects of the already advantaged groups.

In order to have a realistic picture, we would need a full statistical picture but this data is simply not available. No one regularly collates and publishes data on women in Scotland, let alone data on black women. Such data would allow for a more accurate position statement and comprehensive monitoring. I can only comment from my own experience and observation.

In terms of employment, factors like age, family circumstances and education affect the types of jobs women aspire to or are channelled into. The internal gender divisions of each ethnic group will also affect the participation of women in the labour market. What however needs to be addressed is the difficulty black women are faced with when seeking entrance into the job market.

Firstly, there are those who want to enter the job market but cannot for a variety of reasons, eg. lack of qualifications or finance, qualifications which have not been recognised by the establishments in Scotland, poor or non-existent childcare facilities. Secondly, there are those who have entered the job market but have been 'trapped' and 'ghettoised' in the race relations industry, eg. multicultural education workers, race relations advisers, equal opportunities officers or confined to working within the black community, eg. Asian worker with Asian groups. Thirdly, there are those who have qualifications but do not find employment of their choice because of institutionalised and personal racism. The majority of black women who have made it into mainstream employment tend to be in clerical and manual grades with a handful in middle or senior management.

Towards the year 2000, I would like to see more black women gaining access to mainstream employment, recognition by employers of the factors preventing access, eg. racism, non-recognition of equivalent qualifications, poor childcare facilities. It is important that there is a destruction of the stereotypes often associated with black women, particularly Asian female domesticity and cultural constraints. Establishments need to be more imaginative and non-paternalistic in their employment practice. Black women should not be confined to jobs traditionally seen as women's roles or black peoples' roles but should be employed across different departmental functions and across all grades. Black women are not deficits requiring help with entry into the mainstream nor are we second-rate workers. Issues of concern to all women – homeworking, low pay, health hazards, non-unionisation, poor or non-existent childcare provision are of equal concern to us. Our opinions of these must be sought and heard to have the full picture. The importance of bi/multilingualism and the benefits of these should also be remembered.

I have concentrated on employment here but the same applies to other areas – housing, education, health and so forth.

Finding A Voice

We want more control of what is written or produced about us. We have spent the last few years being resources for others – paid and unpaid – assisting in translating policy into action, advising on programmes for broadcasting, interpreting and translating, demonstrating cookery sessions, helping others 'learn' about black women. No one can learn about black women's lives; we are not subject categories, there are no 'in' books to read nor textbooks to study. Black women do not wish to enter the next millennium as pieces of tokenism. We want our own commissions, to write our own scripts, to be our own points of reference and to have our own choices.

What about the concept of sisterhood as global? Whilst women all over share a multiplicity of roles, is that enough of a bond for us to unite? Well, it is a very good place to start. To develop deeper links, white feminist thinking must begin to bear a sense that black women have an indigenous history and traditions of struggle, eg. how women campaigned for reforms in Egypt, agitation of Indian women against dreadful practices like 'sati' (the burning of Hindu widows), the many early women's movements and of course the role of Afro-

Caribbean women and their resistance to slavery. Recently here in Britain/Scotland the resistance against state racism, eg. virginity tests at ports of entry to the UK, against the racist usage of contraceptives like Depo-Provera, against racist attacks on individuals and communities. It would be easy if I could illustrate examples the white women's movement could learn from but it is not about giving examples. It is about understanding where black women are coming from. It is about accepting our different priorities. For me, I have to begin with racism. It is not a choice, it is a necessity. Of course, there are black women who do not recognise that racism occurs but equally, there are women who do not believe in sexism. For the majority of black women, discussions around sexuality and green issues are 'luxury' issues. As stated in the book *The Heart of the Race* by Brayan, Dadzie and Scafe:

'What is the point of taking on male violence if you have not dealt with state violence ?'

It is not that male violence is not an important issue for black women, of course it is but it is also about where we pitch our level. Racial attacks and harassment of us, our children and family are also life and death matters to us. Poverty is also a form of violence we know too well. The white women's movement has made a lot of gains for all women but on the whole they have still failed to address issues of race or class; instead, they have skirted around issues or made excuses for not dealing with them. All women for their own strength and survival need to understand the links between different issues – race, class, gender, to recognise the congruence of all and the specificity of each. Racism within feminism is a reality, to achieve true solidarity with black women means recognising and understanding colonialism, racism and its effects on the lives of black women. We need to examine how racism is operating in Scotland today in all its different guises – to go into this in depth would be the contents of another chapter. We must also celebrate the growth of black self-help initiatives and not feel threatened by them. Allow me (us) to decide how issues like patriarchy oppress me. I recognise sexist structures and practices but as the words of the Combahee River Collective remind us:

'We struggle together with black men against racism, whilst we also struggle with black men about sexism … '

United We Stand

Women have always campaigned for equality and autonomy. It is within these issue-based campaigns that we can begin to work closer together. To improve the quality of black women's lives, the effects and implications of racism just as the effects of sexism and class bias must be recognised as an equal dimension when addressing or campaigning on issues. An example would be in the area of childcare. When campaigning on or discussing this topic, is it also remembered there are different childrearing practices, different dietary requirements, different languages spoken? When purchasing children's books, is thought given that material is free from racial bias as well as gender stereotyping? Is racism recognised as a factor that affects the lives of both black and white children? What of mixed race children?

Our prospects will improve when any significant in-roads for change are made through the persistence of both black and white and not merely left to be the responsibility of the black community. In the meantime, the forward march of black women will not be halted – I move into the future with hope!

a united Europe?

Elizabeth Burns

'Scots ... must think themselves to be Europeans, through travelling and mixing with continentals.' (article in the Business *Scotsman*)

this Europe-country
this floating continent
frontier-less
will it come about
with the issuing of maroon passports
the clipping away of barbed wire fences
the abolition of krone franc drachma
lira peseta pound
with the cramped struggling in schools
over the unwieldy verbs of other languages
or the speaking of a bland and tidy Esperanto ?

can you legislate
for a blending of countries
alter hearts through edicts ?

rather it is stories like this one
that smudge the boundaries
between humans -

when Leonor
who is sleeping on my floor
and who speaks no English
takes me in her arms
and heals a sadness
I have not spoken of

or when I show her the painting
of the garden in Madrid
where she has been amongst the tangly roses
and she pronounces its name, 'Rosaleda'
with some kind of silk around the words
she wears berry colours
and her face is like an almond

there are not enough words
to tell the story of her life
and her lined skin

or to explain his, Antonio's
strange, perhaps blind, eye
but that does not matter
reasons and old facts do not matter
as, with his infinite gentleness
he kisses each of my cheeks
or lets his tongue clamber
slowly and softly
over the sounds of English words

and coming home late and tired
I find on the table
an enormous
Spanish omelette they have made
Antonio divides it into warm pieces
serves it with a glistening salad

and they have filled the blue bowl
with kiwi fruits and bright green apples
we sliver them with knives and eat them
with a pot of mint tea

and talk, in our hampered language
– Antonio going back and forth
between English and Spanish
linking us on a thread –
and discover we have all just read the same book
– they in Spanish, I in translation –
and how we all thought it was wonderful

Antonio says as they leave
– you must come to Madrid
you must come to Madrid –
and I know there will be
a floor to sleep on
and kisses of welcome
and a weight of love
in the unspoken words
we do not need –

in ways like this
we will make millennium
and from a fractured
lumpy continent
forge possibility
of a golden age

Women And Education In Scotland

Alison Cameron

As the nineties approach, the notion of equal opportunities in education is at last gaining some official credibility. Curricular changes have already had an effect on ingrained attitudes, and traditional male and female preserves are no longer quite as they were. Initial sceptics have come to realise that girls can use a chisel just as skilfully as boys, and the pleasure shown by first-year boys on the successful completion of a dish of cauliflower cheese bears witness to the fact that their masculinity has survived their induction into cookery skills. Legislation has been successful too in bringing about a less divisive approach to routine administration in schools, a vital transition stage to the point where gender may eventually seem secondary to individuality.

Yet optimistic as we should be as we go into the 1990s, we must also gauge realistically the nature and scale of what we are up against. For while it is possible to remember that boys need not always carry the milkcrates, or to use 'he/she' instead of 'he' when writing the next unit, to fully accept the implications of equal opportunities in all aspects of education is another matter. And there are already signs that as we prepare for the logical next stage, *belief* in the abilities of women and men to have an equal say in the conduct of their own lives and those of other people, the hitherto unassailed male hegemony, established over many years in Scottish education, is stirring from its comfortable rut, prepared to defend its position.

Strathclyde Region's 'Sex Equality in the Education Service' (1988) suggests that many aspects of the education system operate in favour of boys and men. The report records that while girls work hard at school and gain comparatively better exam results, their achievements show little correlation with later career success. Girls leave school lacking belief in their own abilities, assuming that their role in life is to follow rather than lead. The promoted/unpromoted balance amongst schoolteachers according to gender is much too marked to be accidental, and in the exposure of this and other statistics a clear message can no longer be avoided. We teach boys and girls every day of their lives that men take decisions and women carry them out. It can hardly be otherwise in a school system where, as the Strathclyde document reveals, a staggering 97% of secondary headteachers are male.

There are a number of ways in which advances in equal opportunities policies will be stymied by a lack of understanding or recognition of the pervasive maleness of the educational establishment. The 'logic of dominance', to use Dale Spender's phrase, leads to an assumption in both men and women that those at the top are there because of merit and not because of a variety of culturally-determined biases. Since those in the most responsible positions are usually men, the assumption is made by both men and women that women are less suited for such posts. Criteria involved in the selection process, or the motivations of the selectors, have rarely been questioned.

The same process is at work in the body of knowledge taught in schools. Scientific breakthroughs appear to be mainly the preserve of men because scientific journals publish their findings; women hardly seem to have made any impact on our history because men have defined the world in terms which largely exclude women's sphere of influence. The male editor of *Twelve Modern Scottish Poets* chose a cast of men to convey the essence of Scottish experience to school pupils, for what other set of perceptions was relevant? Maleness-as-norm, by its nature invisible and hence pervasive, is entrenched in our curriculum. Enlightened teachers may carefully avoid stereotyping insofar as they have a choice, but secondary syllabuses are determined largely by the Scottish Examination Board and, less directly, by the universities. The choice of authors to be studied by Higher English candidates in 1990 is revealing in this respect: only one out of nine authors prescribed for study is female (Emily Bronte). At CSYS level the ratio is similar: 3 female authors to 31 male authors represent the literary canon. This assuredness that only male experience, cleansed by years of academic sanction, is worthy to be taught, is a major impediment to any advances we can make in encouraging girls to grow into women confident in their heritage and in encouraging boys to grow into men who will make space for alternative perspectives and versions to theirs.

Why is the curriculum we teach so thirled to male experience? And why in the light of so much evidence of its discriminatory effects is there not more will to change it? Both men and women, themselves brought up in the understanding that male experience is what matters, are liable to pass on what they have been taught to the next generation. Resistance to new ideas is inevitable for this reason. Yet the perpetuation of maleness in educational thinking is inseparable from the predominance of men in top posts in secondary schools and in the Scottish Education Department. Women seldom represent as many as a third of those invited to serve on the committees which advise on educational policy, despite forming some two-thirds of the teaching force as a whole. While a rather fairer balance exists in primary education than was the case twenty years ago, this may have more to do with allowing women to develop within their own traditional sphere of activity than with a belief that what they have to offer in other respects matters.

The ambience created by male hierarchies in both central and regional education authorities is hardly ever advanced as a reason why women do not apply for jobs. Yet despite a professed desire to have more women in leading roles in education, the disincentives created by male exclusivity are considerable. Years of headteachers' gatherings where a milieu of smoke, booze, golf-fixtures and shared assumptions have informed the proceedings make the introduction of women into the club as bizarre as the incursion of privates into the officers' mess. There lingers a degree of suspicion and even misogyny in attitudes to women members of staff. Tribal superstitions prevail in certain outposts of academia. One headteacher is alleged to disapprove of women teachers wearing trousers on the grounds that it is 'unhygienic'. Others are reported as having stated their intention 'never to appoint a woman'. Stories abound of times when 'a woman' was appointed to a senior post and turned out to be a disappointment, leading to the resolution not to repeat the mistake. Ironically the recent appointment of a woman as secondary headteacher has already led to complaints that her gender must have been the reason for an appointment which should have gone to a man. Meanwhile women, even to well-intentioned interview panels, may turn out to be less than 'eminently suitable' for the post, an eminence which may have more to do with the bulges being in the right places than the interviewers themselves are aware. It is small wonder that women do not apply in the numbers they should: their expectations of success are not high.

Resistance to the idea of a woman in a controlling position in education may be put down partly to territorialism and partly to a fear of the unknown. But besides the race knowledge that the depute rector in a school must be the 'hatchet man', that the dark-suited assistant rectors must be prepared to down tools to a man and race to the scene of a pitched battle in the playground, and that senior women will give out aspirins, it can be argued that the language of educational reports has created a male- and female-specific language which has stereotyped men and women in the roles of managers and the unpromoted nurturers of young children respectively.

Women are seldom referred to as such in educational reports. 'He' rather than 'she' has been the generic pronoun employed to denote child and teacher, with girls and women virtually invisible except in reference to, for example, the teaching of needlework. The Primary Memorandum of 1965, however, uses 'she' wherever the ordinary classroom teacher is being referred to. In this seminal document, such descriptions as 'optimistic' and 'cheerful', 'lively, keen and receptive' characterise a good primary teacher, qualities invoking youth rather than the experience and judgement required of someone in a position of authority. Motherliness too is suggested in the references to 'fostering' and 'nurturing', and in the warning to teachers not to 'over-sentimentalise' their attitudes to the children. The use of the generic 'she' to describe the primary teacher has almost certainly helped to influence the kind of educational environment being envisaged for the child in this sector of education. In the rare instances where primary headteachers are referred to by the generic 'she', (an example is the COPE document from 1983 entitled 'Primary Education in the Eighties') there tends to be reference to a style of management which invokes interaction, cooperation and communication rather than the more dynamic thrusting presence envisaged in much literature for secondary headteachers. Such terms as 'support', 'sustain' and 'community' create a humanising rhetoric where the needs of the individual child tend to be emphasised.

By contrast, a look at some of the secondary management reports of the 1980s reveals the distance which exists between qualities espoused in some of the primary documents of the past 25 years, where women can be comfortably accommodated, and the qualities valued in the upper ranks of secondary education. Since 1965 and particularly in the late 1980s, the language of management has become inflated as conviction has grown that improved managerial techniques will solve many problems in Scottish Education. And in this field, stereotypical male attributes are evident. In the 1986 Main Report on teachers' pay and conditions, the headteacher is seen as 'channelling' the 'driving force for change'; he must 'instil a spirit of unity and ... develop ... the "school ethos"'. An externalised, interventionist approach is valued as is a certain capacity for ruthlessness in the interests of efficiency. 'Exploit', 'steer', 'monitor' and 'oversee' are verbs in common currency in, for example, the HM Inspectorate Report of 1984 on school management, all indicating objectivity and detachment. A rigid observance of hierarchy is a central feature, with an emphasis on procedure and control very different from the warmth, liveliness and approachability of the teacher envisaged in the Primary Memorandum. Interesting too in terms of what has been said about the 'youth' imagery invoked in describing the archetypal (female) primary teacher is the use of the word 'senior' to convey rank. Thus on a number of counts the imagery used of women in educational reports is incompatible with that used of managers in secondary schools, indicating that women may find that their spheres of influence in education are limited to those where they have been judged to belong.

More generally, women's say in education is circumscribed by culturally determined notions about what it is to be successful and to lead in any field. For women achieving the first of these (in terms of 'womanhood') has often meant paradoxically the abnegation of self; the second has often attracted vilification rather than admiration. Aggressive, competitive behaviour in women is not admired and may be 'put down' by such epithets as 'pushy', 'strident' and 'hysterical'; men exhibiting the same traits might be described as 'committed' or 'determined'.

Where does all this leave women, and education, in the 1990s? Can we hope, in the move towards equality of opportunity and the recognition of the marginal position of women in the government of education, for a move towards the kinds of skills and emphases long associated with women in primary education? Or will the male stranglehold on education, and the external, institutional approach which seems to be identified with this, merely tighten its grip? If the latter, women will continue to have to compete in an unequal battle for power in a field which educational documentation has defined as being outwith women's sphere of expertise.

Once more an analysis of current educational jargon provides a way of approaching these questions, and the auspices for the millennium look unpromising. In the Thatcherite years the preoccupation with market forces has been applied to education in such a way that education is coming to be regarded in the same terms as any business in which investment is made and from which financial return is expected. Economic terms (such as 'curriculum *audit*') have replaced scientific terms to justify educational decisions and priorities. 'Monitoring' and 'accountability' have come to the fore as solutions to educational problems, and the model of management which will achieve these aims appears to owe little to the cooperative, interactive approach associated with women in educational documentation. Increasingly, recognition of the 'human' dimension in education and the value issues which accompany it seem submerged in a debate whose terms are almost entirely those of the marketplace.

It is in the context of the prevalence of the male viewpoint, endorsed by the priorities of the late 1980s, that we must now see the bid for equal opportunities in schools. Although awareness of the effects of the 'hidden curriculum' of gender assumptions and pupil achievement is becoming more widespread, the recognition of a constructed male hegemony in education has been slow to follow. Stereotyping of women in teaching as skilled only in their ability to communicate with and nurture small children, together with the male-based language of management now current, makes it difficult for women to be perceived as valid applicants for management posts in education. And the signs are that the caring, nurturing dimension to educational discourse has been overtaken by the more institutional concerns of accountability, efficiency and control associated with male stereotypes. Meantime those in power, men, are charged with enacting fairly policies which both undermine their own position and challenge their perceptions of the natural order of things. As we approach the 1990s, we can hardly expect an easy passage.

Dreams in Cold Storage

KAY CARMICHAEL

Most of my childhood was spent in a women-only world. Five of us; my mother, grandmother, two aunts and myself lived in a room and kitchen on the ground floor of a tenement in Glasgow's East End. We shared two hole in the wall beds. Three of us slept in the four foot wide one in the kitchen, two in the two foot six one in the 'room'. In spite of a pervading emphasis on modesty, there was little privacy to be found except by going to the outside lavatory at the back of the close.

All bathing, hair washing, clothes washing and cooking took place in the kitchen. Reading the other day about the horror being expressed about the conservationist suggestion that women use reusable sanitary towels, I was reminded of the bucket of cold water laid down at the side of the sink where my aunts put their bloody cloths to soak every month before my grandmother washed them. We lived in constant awareness of our bodies.

In later years I found no difficulty in understanding why women living in that way had problems about birth control. Before the pill we were dependent on Dutch caps and douching. The lack of privacy was an insurmountable barrier preventing most women from using these methods. Inside lavatories and bathrooms made an untold contribution to middle class women's personal power over their fertility.

But in spite of living in a female household I was surrounded by a culture dedicated to male needs. In neighbours'
houses I could see how men were cared for. They were given
the best piece of meat, the creamy top of the milk and
although in conversation among the women, they were put
down, derided and talked about as if they were wee boys,
their needs came first, before even the children.

That was not surprising. The economy of the family was
totally dependent on the men being healthy enough to go to
work and to stay in work. Memories of the workhouse still
lived fearfully in my grandmother's generation. My lively
young aunts were dedicated to the task of finding a man who
could give them security and the status that went with it. They
had seen in their mother's life the fall in fortunes of the
widow. They saw in my mother's life the struggle of the
separated single parent with no income except what she could
earn in a market which gave single, childless women preference over mothers and young women preference over older
women. They wanted to hold on to the title of 'girl'. I saw
through their eyes the panic of their unmarried women friends
who worked in the large department stores in town where
women were sacked when they lost their youthful looks. Hair
had to be dyed, years deducted from age when applying for
another job.

These were some of the factors that influenced my feminism. I read *The Second Sex* as soon as it was published and of
course Friedan, Greer, Firestone and the rest as they came
along. I was excited and impressed but always found it difficult to relate my own experience to the middle class women I
was beginning to meet who were such vociferous standard
bearers for the women's liberation movement. Too many of
them, it seemed to me, saw the bed as the battleground and

the vagina and the penis as the weapons in the struggle. Sometimes there was an almost pornographic flavour in their emphasis on the sexual dimension of liberation.

For me the struggle lay in equal opportunities for education, work, a parity of esteem which could not be gained while there were still women living in poverty and oppression – women without power. While this continued there would always be a reservoir of women whom men could degrade, not only sexually but in so many other ways – through the exploitation of insecure jobs at minimal wages and inhuman working conditions, and through slavery to a family which men could leave if they chose.

I saw space, privacy and what my mother had always told me – having your own shilling in your hand – as liberation. But the high profile women's movement went for the easy option of polemic and often sneered at those women who set themselves the slow, often tedious, goals of working for change through committees, in churches, voluntary organizations, political groups, even in their work settings. A group of women architects in Denmark refused to build any house unless it contained a room specifically for the use of the female partner in the household. What a creative and revolutionary statement about redistributing power!

The women who have achieved freedom to refuse sex to their partners have yet to accept responsibility for the women who stand on pavements offering sex to any man who will pay for it. Those who have the power to limit the numbers of their children are linked to the Dublin women still fighting for the right to make public information about access to abortion. Those able to eat in expensive restaurants are linked to those washing their dirty plates behind the swinging doors for £1.50 an hour. As long as these things happen, not only in this country but in the economically underdeveloped countries, none of us can be really free.

So I am disappointed when I meet women who think the battle has been won. They say that there is no longer any need to make choices between feminine and masculine roles. They can have everything. I see today's able, well-paid, young women who have emerged into the nineties thinking they have triumphed because they are now able to behave as aggressively and selfishly as any man. They assume that equality lies in their ability to make as insensitive an invitation to share a sexual experience as a man might. Yet they are willingly exploited by clothes designers, make-up advertisers and image makers. They have fallen into the trap of thinking that liberation can be claimed by individuals responding to impulse rather than as part of a philosophy of new human relationships.

At the same time we hear explosions of male rage against feminists who appear to threaten male dominance. Fourteen women were massacred in Montréal by a man who saw his personal image of masculinity being challenged. In America middle class men are crowding into 'workshops' where they hope to rediscover their male identity which they feel has been stolen from them. They are no longer given respect simply for being male, they are no longer sole providers for the family, they feel contaminated by the assumptions that all men are potential rapists and child molesters. Rather than coming closer together in mutual understanding and respect men and women are drifting further and further apart.

Over the past ten years, rising unemployment, a decline in the wages of the lowest-paid workers and the growth in the numbers of lone parents mean that large numbers of women are worse off than they used to be rather than better off.

Women with children, dependent on State benefits, are ground down in poverty; more women, particularly young women are homeless; more are having to care for elderly relatives. An untalked about problem is the numbers of women unable to let themselves become pregnant because their jobs are necessary to pay the high mortgage rates.

Those who have babies and see no alternative but to go back to work are often unable to find decent child care. Mothering, in spite of the Prime Minister's political rhetoric about the family, is still undervalued and not given financial recognition. Most male partners take a minimal share of responsibility for either child care or household responsibilities. And often women put no pressure on them to take a fair share. Instead they are grateful if they are given help.

In essence, the structures haven't changed. We live in a hierarchical society where everyone expects to be subservient to someone and superior to someone else. It applies to the kind of car you have and it applies to personal relationships. The idea of equality of esteem seems sometimes to be too hard for people to grasp. Yet that is what we have to aim for – a world in which men and women can relate to each other without the masks of power and gender we currently wear.

Some of us thought that personal and sexual relationships between women might be free of the oppression we had previously associated with men's power. We hoped that a new model might be created. We have been forced to admit that this has not happened. These relationships have shown themselves to have the same capacity for joy and sorrow and also for cruelty and exploitation, which we previously associated with heterosexual relationships. Child sexual abuse studies are identifying a proportion of women as abusers against both boy and girl children. We have to acknowledge the shadow side of women's lives too.

These are important lessons taught us in the last ten years. To put evil outside ourselves and project it on to another individual, group or class of people is to deny responsibility, not only for our individual power, but for what goes on in the world. The pain that women have suffered in their oppression has been most creatively transformed, not by individual achievement, but by taking it out into the world and trying to change the social roots of oppression.

Women are doing this in South Africa, in Mexico, and in Algeria where on International Women's Day five thousand women marched through the streets of Algiers demanding equality, the right to work and to divorce and an end to discrimination against girls in schools. Women in Scotland united in this way during the Miner's Strike. We know we have strong women with the capacity to reason and organize. Can we only do it when oppression is obviously brutal, not hidden in rural poverty or on ghetto council estates?

In wealthy, industrialized countries like our own, the seductions are powerful. We are bombarded by images of the rewards of success in a man's world. We think we can have it all and mould our feminism to beat men at their own game. We can't. Capitalism and patriarchy are indivisible. At the heart of an undiluted market economy lies a theory which justifies inequality of economic power. That economic power is held by men, and while women are increasingly allowed to flutter on the periphery, only those who show themselves to be as greedy, selfish, ruthless and 'realistic' as the captains of industry will be allowed into the inner sanctums of power.

I'm not interested in how many women achieve that dubious honour. Nor am I interested in attacking them for the path of self-interest some have followed. In order to survive some women have developed a range of coping skills, not all of which are attractive. They have learned to be more coolly manipulative than men as well as seductively charming. As long as personal and social rewards are defined, as they are, in the crude currency of money and power, these skills will be seen as valuable and will continue to be used to counterbalance male power. Women consistently relying on these skills will damage their humanity in the same way that men relying on competition and aggression have damaged theirs.

For me the task for women is for them to use their feminism in life-affirming and creative ways, healing the social divisions between the powerful and the powerless, the rich and the poor, men and women. Twenty years ago there was a strong thread in the women's movement which was asking, not just for 'equality', but for a transformation of Man/Woman relationships – totally new human relationships – a new kind of society. We believed feminism had a special contribution to make – a contribution which had its roots in the experience of our own oppression and an identification with all other oppressed people, men as well as women. We wanted to substitute cooperation for competition, interdependence for dependency, the capacity for joy rather than the capacity to endure. Is there anyone out there who remembers our dreams?

Flower Presser

Ann Coltart

But she was beautiful. Stood in this silly little scrap of a garden with old-fashioned smells in it. Those little purple flowers the bees always liked and then half a hedgeful of red and creamy roses.

Sheena remembered the mauve odour from when she was little, on other people's grannies – slow, shapeless bodies covered with drab colours, noses dulled under powder and wafts of that smell rising from them.

She stared over the gate at the woman in the tiny garden. Everything was very still – the air, thick with the blossomy smells, Sheena tensed beside the hedge and the woman, looking up into the sky, in a pale blue frock and a floral pinafore, with hands loosely clasped in front of her.

She was beautiful and Sheena did not like dealing with that to begin with. The small body, held together peacefully in the warmth with her upturned head gazing at nothing, hinted at ideas like grace, harmony, even sensuality, though she was supposed to be beyond the age where certain senses counted.

Irritated by her own stare, when this person was just an ancient unit who had lived quite long enough, Sheena put her hand on the gate and thought she'd better get things started.

'Hello, is that Mrs. Cordell?' she called, dead sweet when it was called for, she knew. She pressed her body against the gate and leaned her head over it, grinning beside a rose which stank of its own brief sweetness. The little figure shifted, hands unclasping to shield her eyes as the head turned slowly towards the voice at the gate. 'What a day,' said the woman in the garden. 'Isn't it just?' She lifted her feet slightly, one by one, as though they had gone to sleep. 'Who is it, love?'

She started moving across the grass towards the gate, smiling, taking tiny steps, though without tottering. Her hair was cloudy white, her skin still smooth across the bones, though crinkled in soft areas beneath a chin still pointed, around the eyes and lips. As she came closer, Sheena was again a little shaken, by the palest eyes, worn away by light, it seemed, but with hints of many colours. 'It's not Isa,' said the woman, who stopped as Sheena opened the gate and clicked her heels on to the short, paved path running to the door of the cottage. 'You are Mrs. Cordell, aren't you?' she asked, as the gate swung to behind her. 'Yes of course I am. Don't you know me? Lilian. Cordite Lil. Whatever next. I don't know.'

This old woman, 93 years old on Sheena's list, suddenly giggled and clutched her diaphragm. 'Oh god, I'm sorry love. I've had so many names. Come in, come in.'

Sheena felt almost resentful. It was all too easy. Here was she prepared for a thousand awkward moments, twice as many tactics for dealing with them and a few million brain cells charged up. 'Listen, Mrs. Cordell,' she said sharply. 'You should be more careful, I'm just from the centre, you know, seeing if you need anything done. But you're here on your own and you ... you're not really young anymore.'

Mrs. Cordell gazed at her with those pale, direct eyes and immediately started chuckling again. 'Oh my dear, I'm scared silly,' she said, still shaking with laughter. 'You'll all be the death of me, you will.'

She smiled gently into Sheena's face and turned to step ahead of her to the open door. Sheena followed the slow, unworried limbs. It seemed there was going to be no problem, apart from leaving the house afterwards. But she had a faded cotton jacket and headscarf crushed in her bag for that. She would just be another nobody making her way down the road to the railway station. 'We'll go into the kitchen, won't we, hey?' said Mrs. Cordell. 'Come on and find yourself a seat and shift anything if you need to. I do make the place a mess but life's too short to spend on your knees scrubbing and wiping. Isa grumbles when she comes in sometimes but she enjoys it really. Now, would you like some tea, or will I give you some elderflower fizzy champagne? Just the day for it.'

Closing the front door, Sheena walked into the kitchen. There was a fat red cushion in a wicker chair which would do the job. Get the woman sitting down first and settled, then swiftly pick up the cushion, hold the back of her head with one hand and press the cushion hard and downwards with the other. It shouldn't take long. The woman was small and slight, if not as frail as she ought to be. 'Fizzy what?' she asked, looking at the serene Mrs. Cordell again.

The matter suddenly felt more complicated. An anonymous body half-dead already was how she'd viewed the situation when she had offered to do the job. The woman's beauty had unnerved her slightly. That was a freakish problem she should deal with, but all this life, this Cordite Lil fizzy stuff was not on the jobsheet. 'Fizzy what. Fizzy what,' repeated Mrs. Cordell. 'Yes, let's have some fizzy what and you call me Lily. I used to pick the blossoms myself, but now Isa brings them in, every year. And when the berries come, I still make the elderberry wine. You could have some of that if you like, from last year, but the champagne's good on a hot day.' 'That will be lovely,' said Sheena. 'Who's Isa?'

The woman disappeared into a pantry off the kitchen and came out with a bottle of clear, cream-coloured liquid. 'What's that, love?' she asked, taking a couple of glasses from a shelf and putting them on the table with the bottle. 'Yes, you call me Lily, like everyone does. I know you've only come to do me a kindness. From the centre. And what's your name?'

She sat down suddenly on a hard kitchen chair behind the table. 'Go on, you open it,' she said. 'Now I see you better, I think you must be about the same age as my great, yes, great-granddaughter. Funny that, isn't it? Great and grand. Sad, though. I haven't seen her since she was about ten. All the others are dead. There's only little Moira left, but she might turn up one of these days. I send her cards, but young people move around now, don't they?'

Little Moira. Sheena twisted savagely at the bottle. Little Moira was the one who'd sent her here and the work was already getting messed up with talk and smells and champagne and laughing and the things you don't generally have to think about. 'You must have seen a few people off, Lily,' she murmured as she poured out the sparkling liquid. A delicate, faintly acid fragrance rose from the glasses as they spat the rising bubbles. 'Who's Isa, though? Does she live here?'

Lily laughed again gently, lifted her glass and sniffed it and then put it back on the table. 'Off? Yes, I've seen them off, I suppose,' she said. 'But they all stay with you, don't they? The loved ones are always here and there's always been a lot of that. Have you found that? I don't suppose you've known many dead people yet, though. Oh dear, I'm going off again, amn't I? Isa has a good go at me sometimes but she loves my wicked tales. She comes round to do the home help and spends half her time sitting here laughing. Better for her, I say.

Who cares about a bit of grime? What's your name then, love?'

Sheena had a name ready, in case something went wrong. It lay on her tongue easily, but as she took a sip of the fizz, the cool foaming left unfamiliar scents in her throat, spreading up behind her nose. The name began to contract, wouldn't come. 'Sheena,' she answered clumsily. 'Sheena.' Lily breathed the word as though it were a precious thing. 'Makes you think of long, gleaming hair, doesn't it? I used to know a Seonaidh. Must have been about 70 years ago. She went marvellous mad. With love, it was. And she was married to him. But she got over it, I think. Do you love strongly? I always do, but not madly, perhaps.'

Sheena stared at her. The price for pressing the life out of this creature was slipping off the scale of things. What did the woman have? A few more years, a funny little house with a few old flowers outside and a bundle of dusty papers in a bank she probably didn't know the value of nor thought about. Though little Moira, sick of waiting, had decided to get hold of them some swiftly final way.

Moira's envoy began, unusually, to feel out of her depth, stupid, sitting sipping something made out of squashed flowers, almost relaxed and interested in this ancient woman, when she should be squashing her against a plump pillow. Cordite Lil was watching her curiously across the table, her shining white head on one side, a touch teasing. 'Don't mind me,' she said. 'I come out with everything. Always have. It's cleaner, don't you think, Sheena? There are plenty of mysteries already.'

The younger woman said nothing and nibbled against the glass rim at her lips. 'Anyway,' went on Lily, 'I expect I'll be shut up for good, one of these days, but this old machine just loves charging on. I've been in love, you know, most of the time. I'm in love now and I feel it will keep me going a thousand years. Isn't that a bit mad, Sheena, or is it sense?'

Madness seemed to be collecting in Sheena's lap. She needed Moira's money badly, but she just sat there, holding her empty glass and looking back at Lily's faded eyes, thinking about mysteries. 'I don't know,' she said finally. 'I'm not very good at that sort of thing, I suppose. Love and so on. I'm not much good at anything, really.'

Lily smiled again and pointed at the bottle. She swallowed some of her own drink. 'Go on, there's plenty more,' she said. 'Pour it out. It always gets Isa misty when she has a drop and you should see my boy's eyes gleam after a tumbler. Beautiful he is, Robbie. Turns my heart over every time he comes round. From the centre. My Robbie. You'll know him. He turns my old heart over and he knows it because I tell him.'

Sheena got to her feet and saw the large red cushion only a couple of feet away. She looked down at Lily and saw that the soft cheeks were blushing, the eyes brimming. There was silence and Sheena leaned forward to pour another drink.

She would just sit here a little longer and then leave for the train. It was too hot for the jacket and scarf anyway she thought. She would tell Moira she would have to wait, and so would she. It wasn't a very bright way to do the business, but she would think about that later.

The old woman dabbed her eyes with the corner of her floral apron and looked up at the young woman roguishly. 'Lavender,' said Sheena. 'That's the stuff in your garden with all the bees. I haven't smelled it while it's growing, not for a long time.'

She sat down again and raised her glass.

The Millennium Hot Air Balloon

Janet Davidson

So we are approaching the millennium. Two thousand years from an arbitrary point in the history of a small part of the globe as recorded by men. In terms of the existence of life in some form on Earth, two thousand years is a hiccup.

This planet has been moving steadily through space for millions of years. She moves at the same rate now as she did at the beginning. It still takes a measured, regular period for her to turn on her own centre, to make the circuit of her source of energy. Like any female, she has her rhythms but can still adjust herself to absorb change and hurt – while providing care, shelter and food.

As we approach this supposed landmark, we are seeing an upsurge in interest in this world as a possibly finite thing. The media are suddenly using weighty words like Environment and Pollution, the Quality of Life. 'People' it seems are destroying the ozone layer, the rain forests. 'People' are using up the world's resources, creating poisonous waste.

Make no mistake, the clouds of sulphur dioxide now devouring the layers of gas which protect all terrestrial life from excessive exposure to the sun's output of energy are not caused by the actions of 'people'.

They are created and fed by the vast barrage balloon of words which men have invented in praise of their own activities.

The rain forests are not being sacrificed to make someone a living. Every acre destroyed goes ultimately to feed the egos of those men who control the timber companies, the construction companies, the catering chain companies, the political parties, by inflating the image they present to other men of their power.

It is not 'people' who choose to solve their problems by war, having institutionalised their inability to compromise in the production of ever more horrific weapons. It is men. And it is the development, manufacture and deployment of military machinery which most wastefully use natural resources and create the most noxious waste.

Men have taken for themselves the power to make decisions about how this world is run. They talk about Good and Right and Truth, cosily ensconced in reserved areas – Studies, Offices, Chambers, Clubs, Board Rooms, Operations Centres. They pontificate on things over which they have no influence while absenting themselves from areas where they should be active and concerned.

Meantime, women carry out the tasks which make it possible for the human race to continue – feeding, loving, clothing, cleaning, touching. They understand that the resources they have at their disposal are limited, that happiness cannot be bought and that real pleasure lies in small things, small events. Their bodies remind them of their reality and connection with the life of this planet.

It is time to pierce the great bag of hyperbole which men have filled with the hot air of their self-aggrandisement. Let us examine a sample of these noxious gases.

Religion: how is it that most deities are male, that we are expected to recognise an all-knowing, all-loving *Father*?

Any woman, most children, most truthful men, could tell

you that male parents are, at best, part-time carers who talk a lot about the Importance of Family Life but invariably give priority to their Work or leisure pursuits which rarely include partners and children. They demand time and attention for themselves while providing minimal emotional support. At worst, Fathers are a source of misery, using the power bestowed by strength and custom to control and abuse their partners and children.

Surely early humans would have revered the female who could produce living bodies from within her own and provide food from that same body. I believe that men invented Gods with male characteristics to make up for their own feelings of inadequacy in the face of this overwhelming miracle. Gods they could control and use to control others ... and with those Gods came Bishops and Popes and Ministers and Maharashis ...

The result has been the deliberate downgrading of maternal, female traits – co-operation, strength in suffering, the expression of feelings, good humour, caring, neediness.

What about football? It isn't surprising that people enjoy chasing, kicking and throwing a ball about. It's good exercise, good fun and a nice way to spend time with people you like. But World Cup Football, the Football Association, the League, UEFA, the National Sport bear very little resemblance to *fun*.

Thousands of predominantly male spectators shuffle up narrow stairways to stand or sit on concrete terraces, bawling at twenty-two overpaid dots on a distant patch of green. They cannot really know the players or identify them with the place where they live. So why do they talk about the Lads and the Home Team and Our Club and wear silly hats and scarves? What all those thousands of men are really saying is 'This is a great thing to do because we're all doing it together and we're men.'

The pages of hysterical nonsense written about football take up more room in popular newspapers than copy about any other subject, even when no games are being played. Equivalent space is not given to the concerns of women and children. Few resources are put at their disposal for activities they might care to pursue.

One of the Great Thinkers of our Century, Herr Doktor Freud, found himself asking the frequently-quoted question 'What do women want?' Women know what they want, but have been confused, frightened into thinking that it is not acceptable. By current, male-manufactured and imposed standards it is too small scale, too personal, too subjective, not for the Greater Good of all Mankind. They want to enjoy the companionship of those they care about in some degree of comfort and safety. That is precisely what the earth has evolved to provide for all forms of life.

What Dr. Freud really could not understand was why women did not want what men wanted which is, it seems, to have the power to validate the picture they have painted of and for themselves.

Most of this picture is pure fantasy.

We are led to believe that men protect women and children from danger and provide for them, that they are the source of all progress while women tag along behind; that the relationship between men and women is paramount over all others; that men love women.

You do not defend your children and their mother by abandoning them and your home to fight with other men.

You do not make peace possible by creating and using weapons which maim, kill, fry or evaporate living creatures including humans.

You do not show your love for women and concern for children by using them as sexual chattels, by creating a market for or condoning prostitution; by rape or by consuming pornography. Or even by tolerating the exploitation of their vulnerability in 'glamour' pictures.

You do not contribute to progress by placing quantity before quality. You may become the Head of the Largest Company in the World, envied by other men who share the same empty dreams.

You cannot buy more than 24 hours in the day. You cannot control the way the earth turns or the way things evolve. You can destroy people, plants, animals. You can avoid having close relationships but you will not be contributing in any way to progress.

Life continues because every life form has survival as its first priority. The pre-requisite for this is the co-operation of the mature of each species in looking after the immature. Where, as in the human race, one part of the equation undervalues and exploits the other and behaves in a way which threatens the survival of its young, that species is in severe danger.

It is women who have kept this race going, inching forward, by giving the time, effort and commitment to caring for each other, for the children. Despite rather than because of what men do. They even care for men and continue to hope, against overwhelming evidence, that they may find one willing to return the emotional support they offer. A cool look at their relationships would show that they have more fun, relaxation and closeness in their relationships with each other.

Women *must* stand up, take each other's hands and say one

enormous, crashing, reverberating NO which will pierce the dangerous squelchy bladder of Presidents, First Secretaries, Corporations, Clinical Obstetricians, Ayatollahs, Directors, Your Honours, etc. Pierce it and let out the evil poison of pornography, prostitution, child abuse, terror, pain and self-delusion which lurk behind the titles.

Women have been trained, bred to believe they are unable to change their situation. We have been deliberately isolated from power and from each other in what men have defined as our sphere. No clubs, societies, meeting places provided for women. We have been confused into forgetting that women are half of the human race. Not help-mates to men. Not machines to breed workers for men's distorted idea of progress. Not helpless, weak creatures only surviving by male grace and favour, but strong, integral and naturally empowered.

If we trusted each other instead of accepting the idea that only men can affect our lives, we could have all the power we needed. Not to overwhelm others. Not to rule them in turn, but to bring the emphasis of all our lives back towards the personal, to pleasure. This world is to be enjoyed, not to be overpowered.

It is time to call men's bluff. It is my hope that the millennium will be the turning point in humanity's history – the point when women take back their natural place in the scheme of things.

Name A Dozen Women Artists

Rosie Furlong

... straight off. Well, there's Bridget Riley. Her with the wriggly lines. And there's Berthe Morisot, but they didn't seem to think much of her, because she just painted things to do with the family, like a woman gazing at a child sleeping in a cot, or children picking cherries, whereas important artists did things like a man pushing a woman on a swing, or dancing in the park, or rowing on the river, so she didn't really reach her full potential you know. No, I'm not trying to evade the issue, I can name a dozen easy. There's Joan Eardley, poor thing, and the sculptor, sculptress I mean. I was right the first time? Oh, I thought these terms were dignified by ancient usage. Yes, well, right enough, I see what you mean. Anyway, Hepstein, I'm talking about. Hepworth, was it ? Well, you know who I mean. Barbara Hepworth, I was close enough. SHE might not have thought so? I suppose not. Never mind, don't distract me! And there's another one, isn't there? The one who's a Dame now. Frink, that's it, Lizzie Frink. She does other things besides big eagles, doesn't she? And there's Laurencin and Valadon, Utrillo's mum – you know she never had a lesson in her life, except the help she got from Degas, but that doesn't really count does it ? Because it was just advice and paper and stuff he gave her, not like real instruction ... Okay, okay I'm getting on with it. Gwen Jones. And they say that she'd have been better than Augustus if she hadn't devoted herself to looking after Rodin. Who else? Peggy O'Keefe. No, wait a minute, she plays the piano, doesn't she? Georgia, that's right, Georgia O'Keeffe. And ... there were quite a lot in the past, weren't there? But they weren't so famous, of course, because they were, well, because they were women I expect. That reminds me, there's Grandma Moses – she was also an artist. She had her vision. She was a naïve painter, just like Rousseau, though he was a man. There's quite a few in Scotland, now, isn't there? Artists who are women, like Blackadder and Low. Sounds like a pop group doesn't it? Chas and Whatshisname? Is she related to the grocers, do you think? They're all con-glomerations now though, aren't they? That must be just about the dozen now, isn't it? A second dozen? Well, there's her who painted the hop-pickers. Funny we were talking about her yesterday for some reason. The name will come to me. Dame Laura – another Dame you see. And there's Mary Cassatt, the American – she's quite famous as Degas' pupil, isn't she? And there's Sophie, Mrs Arp, and there's Diego's Mrs as well, and there's Miss Mary, or Mary Miss, is it? Her with the JCB's. Then there's the other Mary, who worked with surfaces, Martin was it? Mary Martin, it was. I knew all the time. And there was Käthe Kollwitz who did the refugees in charcoal. She was married to a doctor, of course. There was a Judith Leyster too, or something like that, an old Dutch Mistress, you might say. And there were Toshie's lot, his Mrs, she was a well-known artist in her day, wasn't she? What was she called? Margaret Morrison, or MacDonald, or something. How many's that? Twenty one, not bad, straight off. Really, I could get more if I was allowed to look them up. Where? Well, that's a point, isn't it? Still want the other three? What about that humble cleaning lady who painted pictures from God?

Seraphine, that was her name. I always remember that because it seems such a suitable name for her theme, don't you think? Twenty-two. There were all the women associated with the Colourists, who were they again? Anne Something Rice, she had a middle name I can't remember. Very tragic she was, I think. There was a big bit about her in one of the supplements lately, so she must be pretty important. I didn't read it all, of course, because I had to make lunch, but what I did read was very sad. There was a Jessica as well, who painted with them, wasn't there? That's it. Two dozen. A third dozen? You are JOKING? Well there was another Dutch woman who was awfully good at painting tulips. They eventually had to eat all their tulip bulbs, didn't they? The Dutch, I mean. That reminds me, I think I'll make onion soup for dinner. Who was very fond of onion soup? Was it Renoir or Pissarro? I just love onion soup, don't you?

Motherhood, School, And The Millennium

Pat Gerber

Why don't more Scotswomen play a full and equal part in the politics and business life of our country? How can we achieve full representation in the future? And in particular, why do so few of us who are mothers reach the top? The reasons are, of course, complex. We're a modest lot, for a start, not given to pushing ourselves forward. Then there's our apparent partiality for the dominant male – chieftain o' the puddin' race – who we still encourage in his unhelpfulness. There are our folkloric notions of good motherhood. And there is the time-table of education we endorse every time we meekly trot along to collect our children from the school gates, no matter how inconvenient the hour.

Depending on the ages of our children that can be one delivery and two collections per morning, and the same in the afternoons, involving quite a mileage.

Well, it's our job, isn't it? It's part of the price we pay for motherhood. It's what we've been brought up to expect. Politics are for other people.

Picture, along with visitor, Werner Kissling, in the thirties, the guid Scots wife singing as she waulks her tweed, minds her poultry, hefts her peats, turns out a soda scone, all with a dozen children clustered about her beclogged feet. Cut to the year 2000 and visualise, along with groups like A Woman's

Claim Of Right In Scotland, the Scottish Assembly in session in Edinburgh. 52% of its membership is composed of dynamic, intelligent, highly educated, experienced females, proportionately representing more of the same. Who are these women? From where are they to materialise? And how, for goodness sake, are they to get time to do the work?

In this year 1990 they are aged somewhere between nought and nineteen.

So, is the answer to persuade all our cleverest, most caring girls to throw away their dolls, to eschew all the joys of motherhood that tie so many of us irrevocably to child-oriented rhythms and timetables? Shall we select them via some sort of eleven-plus, neuter them and train them up for a selfless vocation in politics and big business, forever forbidden to complicate their lives with personal relationships? And if not, then how can we ensure that all the women of Scotland, including the mothers, are to be adequately and fairly represented on the top rungs of career ladders and in Ministerial positions in politics both here, at Westminster and in Brussels?

One of the biggest considerations career mothers have, apart from that career, is the well-being of their children. Only the younger and more thoughtless feminist can truly believe that bunging children into a créche is sufficient to free the spirit. The brighter the mum, the higher are her aspirations for her offspring. She understands about the quality of life her children need if they are to perform well in their own lives.

Most of us have strong ideals about motherhood, gleaned perhaps from our own mothers or grannies, reinforced by advertising and the media, pressed on us by magazines and writers of child-care books. Few of us doubt that each child has some kind of human right to a reasonably available mother. But, while there's plenty of information available on how to be a good mother, how much is there on how to get to the top in a career once you have children, on the practical steps into local or national politics?

Someone might carry out revealing surveys into how many middle-class mothers choose teaching simply because you get the same school holidays as the children, or the proportion of unqualified mums who opt for ancillary school work for the same reason, or reduce their work-potential to temping as typists or cleaners. Even so, many, especially single mothers, are forced to carry on working when schools are closed, forced unwillingly to leave their children roaming the streets.

Because we care a great deal about the quality of life of our children, we don't want simply to dump them when we go to work. We want them to be doing the sort of things we'd do with them ourselves if we were at home, extending their experience, widening their horizons, and sometimes just having fun. We need to know, not just that our children are safely minded, but that they're having quite an interesting, satisfying time.

Would it not be sensible for the mothers of tomorrow's women to spend the nineties changing the archaic 'system' of education we have inherited from our Victorian male educators into something of more practical use to everyone?

If you are at present a working mother, imagine a year in which there were no separate school terms and holidays, and in which schools opened from, say, 8am till 10pm. You are free to use the vastly improved facilities available therein for your children as much or as little as you want. You may choose when you want to take your children off on holiday with you whenever it best suits you as a family. There's a hostel in which children can stay for anything from one night to five should there be a crisis at home, or when parents have to be away on business.

What would the children be doing all day, cooped up in a classroom while Mum carves out her career? More of the three Rs? However tempting we might find it to say that the present turn towards vocational pragmatism will result in an education which is impoverished both in scope and quality, no.

There are lessons to be learned here from the private sector, if we can find educationalists humble enough to consider these.

For instance, we are told that our children are all heading for heart attacks because they take so little exercise. Yet young children are naturally energetic. See them fidget towards the end of a lesson, watch them afterwards, out in the playground. With a much longer school day there would be lots of time for physical activity. Not the old public-school para-military training of boys in cricket teams, of rugby thugs, but a much more individually-based choice of exercise, some out-of-doors, some sociable, some team-based, some individual.

With more hours spent in a controlled environment, there would be a point in giving pupils work to do on their own – 'homework' – because there would be a time, and a quiet place, set aside in school for them to do it without the distractions of a busy home. This would also give children from deprived areas a better chance of achieving academic equality.

Meals would be provided throughout the day. Social workers and counsellors would be on hand to talk through problems, playleaders and recreation specialists employed to help develop pupils' interests and hobbies in the free hours that would be timetabled into the day.

Who would work such long hours to look after the children? School work would be arranged in shifts or modules, allowing maximum flexibility for all the categories of staff that would be needed. There would be a wide variety of opportunities for part-timers, job-sharers and itinerant experts travelling round several schools in their area, especially in country districts. What tempts people into careers in hotels, factories, hospitals, public transport and the media, all of which require round-the-clock work, is a combination of decent pay and conditions, and a feeling that the work suits their personalities, and that would do nicely for school-workers too.

The new schooling would be State-funded and available to all children from three years old up to fourteen. But it would not be compulsory. Parents must remain free to educate their children in the way they want to, or to do it themselves.

There could be a system of ability-gates through which a child would pass on her way through her education, such as the achievement of reading skills, some standard of numeracy, regardless of her age. It would be illegal for anyone under fourteen to work.

From fourteen up, a child's options would widen dramatically. Secondary schools would also be staying open all year round, but more as an available resource than a compulsory incarceration.

At present one of the hardest things a mother can have to do is to get her pubescent children even to attend school. She may be forced to resort to bribery, attempt coercion, in order to push the rebelling pupil through exams the results of which will affect the course of its entire life. And while some teenagers cope perfectly well, others become disenchanted with education, disrupting classes, playing truant, getting into trouble, breaking the law, learning that education for them spells failure.

Instead, they should be freed to look for work among adults. Even though the jobs they can find may be very basic, the very fact of working alongside adults has a maturing effect. Go into any college of Further Education and compare the attitudes of day-release students with the full-timers. But their right to several years of free education should remain, to be taken if and when required by the individual. Perhaps we should even institute a system of grants for this.

With a set of more realistic guidelines for the education of their older children, and the facilities available for this, working mothers will be mentally and emotionally freed to climb up their own career ladders to the top.

We have invested enormous sums of money in school buildings, many of which are becoming redundant. We should use them, full-time.

The system we have now grew out of reaction and expediency. Any planning was done by men with servant-wives. The working mothers of today don't have wives, but we are still as concerned as our forebears that our children should not suffer deprivation of any kind as a result of our wish to realise the full extent of our potential.

There will still be those who prefer to compromise, or to stay at home, because they believe it's best for their children, and that's fine. There will always be those who, through no fault of their own, have to work so that their children can eat. In order that the bulk of us can be properly represented in business and in the Assembly though, we must push for fundamental changes in the provision of care and education for the families of the women who are capable of performing at the forefront of these careers. And if we ever find ourselves wondering why, now in Scotland's sixth generation of compulsorily-educated children we are not a better society than we are, then we must be interested at least in considering improvements.

For a long time Scotland led the educational field. It is imperative that we find ways to release more of our women to enter public service, to represent us in every organisation in the land. In Scotland we are a small enough community to sort ourselves out, to initiate and implement new ideas. We stooped to being England's guinea pigs for the Poll Tax, surely we have enough motivation to rid ourselves of one of the major inconveniences of maternity before the millennium?

The Senile Dimension

Magi Gibson

1. So sorry, dear,
    To hear, poor dear,
    About your father's
    Senile Dimension.

2. You are riotously funny
    a one-man farce
    you clown around
    toppling the routine
    of all our lives.

    First off there is
    the dressing of you
    Vest over shirt
    Socks over shoes
    Surrealist in Senility.

    At tea-time you babble
    perched on a flip-top bin
    (we really flip our lids at that)
    You spoon butter in brown tea
    Spread sugar on white bread
    then down it all

along with our concern.

You are riotously funny.
Our laughter gives us breathing space
All too soon we know we face
the final scene
of a family tragedy.

3. The baby brings out
    the best in you

    She alone makes contact
    in your broken mind.

    You smile, cajole, cosset
    like any doting grampa.
    She giggles, gurgles while
    for her you speak
    a few syllables of sense.

    The baby brings out
    the best in you.
    Brings smiles to your lined face

    rubs salt in the raw wound
    where life and death are caught
    where only the very young

    and the very old
    are free to laugh and meet.

4. The Machine is broken.
   It will not respond
   to normal commands.
   It operates
   but erratically.

   I have phoned.
   I have phoned.

   The Repair Man cannot call today.

   The Machine is definitely broken.
   Its memory has rewound.
   It jams on replay
   transmits scenes from
   donkeys years ago.

   The Machine is losing power.
   Even its basic functions
   cannot be relied upon.
   I watch it constantly.

   I am afraid of the Machine.
   I think it might be dangerous.
   The children have been warned.
   Someone should unplug it.

   But no-one will.

   I have called the Repair Man.

   The Repair Man cannot call today.

5.　Minnie sings
　　sweet as the mina bird
　　in the jungle of the dayroom.

　　Andy claps the one-man show
　　they stage for him alone
　　in the circus of the dayroom.

　　The window rambles on
　　and on and on
　　with memories of the War
　　the Great Depression and
　　remember wee Aunt Annie
　　to the captive audience
　　it reflects upon
　　in the mystery
　　of the dayroom.

　　Life goes on and on
　　and makes no sense
　　in the hot air
　　of the dayroom.

6.　In the psycho-geriatric ward
　　he slumps, strapped to a seat
　　even you could not struggle out of.

　　In the psycho-geriatric ward
　　he wears slippers
　　which are not his
　　he wears trousers, socks

a shirt which belongs to
no-one.
Not anymore.

In the psycho-geriatric ward
his soul is trapped in a cage
even you could not wriggle out of.

He wears a smile
which is not his
(not like we knew)
He bears a crown of thorns
inside his head
which should be left on
no-one.

And no-one's eyes are closed.
No-one's hands are tied with red tape
he claims is not his
he claims he cannot struggle out of

No-one hangs his head and cries
it's no-one's problem
in the psycho-geriatric ward.

7. So sorry, dear,
    to hear, poor dear,
    about your father's
    Senile Dimension.

Wee Wifey

KATHLEEN JAMIE

I have a demon and her name is
                    WEE WIFEY
I caught her in a demon trap, the household of my skull.
I pinched her by her heel throughout her wily
                                        transformations
until
        she confessed
                    her name indeed to be WEE WIFEY
and she was out to do me ill.

So I made great gestures like Jehova: dividing
land from sea, sea from sky,
                        my own self from WEE WIFEY
(*There,* she says, *that's tidy!*)

Now I watch her like a dolly
keep an eye,
            and mourn her;
for she and I are angry/cry
                    because we love each other dearly.

It's sad to note
                that without
                        WEE WIFEY

I shall live long and lonely as a tossing cork.

Long Grass, Moon City

Helen Lamb

Rose lay in the long grass, watching a big, fat cumulus cloud slowly change shape. The grass was bleached yellow but not yet brittle. It must be three feet high. No – that wasn't right. She was exaggerating. More like two. Up to her knees, anyway. High enough for her to lie there and not be seen by anyone passing by. Rose felt ripe and perfectly content.

James was tugging at her arm but she didn't feel like moving right now. He tugged a bit harder. Then, suddenly, toppled backwards and landed comfortably on his bottom. He looked surprised. Rose grinned. She reached over for her bag and pulled out a packet of rusks. That should keep him quiet for a while. She closed her eyes and drifted off, trying not to fall asleep and spoil the sensation of being in between. She got about twenty minutes before the sound of a radio spoiled her peace. Someone was coming her way. She sighed and opened her eyes. James was still sitting in the same spot with soggy rusk dribbling down his t-shirt. She'd have to change him now.

There were three of them. When Rose sat up they looked over at her. They were about thirteen – maybe fourteen. One of them had black hair with a bit of a wave in it. He looked over at her again and Rose turned her back and began sponging James's face and hands.

'Hey, missis.' The one with the black hair was coming

towards her. He looked like a cocky little bastard – all strut and snigger. 'Huv ye got a light, missis?'

Rose gave him a dirty look. The missis annoyed her. She said, 'Are you not a wee bit young to be smoking, sonny?'

The boy flushed. 'Don't call me sonny.'

'Well don't you call me missis, then. OK?'

The boy stared at her. Rose gave him her matches and he went back to his mates. She turned her back on them and began to change James. She peeled off his t-shirt. Missis. Cheeky little sod. She could be his big sister. She wasn't even twenty yet. She took a clean top out of the bag and looked down at her swollen belly. Not twenty yet and six months gone again. She pulled the clean top roughly over James's head. Soon as you have a baby you're automatically written off as a missis as far as they were concerned. And what was a missis?

She turned to get the talcum powder and saw that the boys were moving off. 'Hey, you. I want my matches back.'

The boy came back and dropped the matches at her feet. She took a dozen or so out and handed them to him. 'Here. You can have these.' The boy said ta. Neither of them smiled.

She watched the boys cross the burn and cut through a gap in the high wire fence. They disappeared into the wasteground behind the scheme, where phase three lay abandoned. Before the foundations had even been finished, the blocks in phase one and two were showing signs of dampness. So phase three had been cancelled and those families in the existing blocks were left to rot – or get out if they could. It wasn't easy to get out.

She lay down and shut her eyes again but it was too late. The boys had spoilt it. If they hadn't come along she might have sung something like – Gershwin. 'Summertime and the living is easy. So hush pretty baby' – slow and soulful. Maybe she could get the mood back. She tried humming it quietly to herself but it didn't work. Her voice wavered. Pathetic – she thought. She wouldn't want anyone to come by and catch her singing like that. When you were a kid, you could sing any way you wanted – anywhere you wanted but she was a mother now.

Sometimes, when it rained, she pushed the pram up to Rouken Glen. There was a waterfall there – right at the back, behind the woods and when it had been raining for a few days, it got really noisy and she would lean over the wooden fence, let the spray wet her face and sing anything that came into her head as loud as she wanted.

When Rose got back, Gordon was out on the deck-access, leaning against the parapet. He must have forgotten his keys. A group of women smiled and said hello to her as she passed. It was nice, the way the sun brought people out of doors – even though the kids made such a racket, trundling up and down on their bikes.

'Hello. You're early.'

Gordon didn't look at her. He said, 'It's Friday.' Gordon didn't look at her much now – not since she got pregnant again. It was ironic really – there she was getting bigger and bigger and more and more invisible as far as he was concerned.

She gave James to his father and hunted through her bag for the keys. 'Don't tell me you've lost them again. Here let me have a look.' He put out a hand to take the bag. He was always in such a hurry. She pulled the bag back from him and went over to the parapet where the light was better and searched through the bag methodically. They were right at the bottom under the polythene bag with the dirty clothes. She handed over the keys and they went inside. 'What kind of day did you have, then? Rose asked.

'The usual.'

'Oh.' Rose was disappointed. Just for once she wished he would pretend to be happy. He put James down to crawl on the carpet and drew his pay packet out of his back pocket. He put it up on the shelf. Rose looked at it. It had been opened. 'Don't worry,' he said. 'I only took my fare home.'

'I wasn't worried,' she said quietly.

'The rest of them were going to the pub.'

'Why didn't you go, too?' As soon as she asked, Rose realised it was a mistake. He gave her one of his frustrated looks that meant he was thinking – this stupid woman doesn't know me at all. He said, 'It's bad enough having to work with that shower of animals without going drinking with them when I've finished.'

He was shouting. Rose said she would go and make the dinner. She lifted James and went through to the kitchen, shutting the door behind her. She stayed there until the food was ready, though all she had to do was switch on the oven. The meal had been prepared earlier. This was one of her organised days. The washing and ironing was up to date. The flat was clean. Everything was in its place and she was in control. This was how it was supposed to be.

They spent the evening watching television. At 9.30, Gordon switched over. There was a programme about submarines he wanted to see. Rose sighed and lit up a cigarette. 'I thought you'd stopped,' Gordon said.

'I'm bored.' She took a long drag and exhaled slowly through her nose. He kept his eyes on the screen. 'Do something then.'

'I'm too tired.' He got up and turned the volume down a bit.

'Where were you today, then?' Rose looked across at him. He was still glued to the submarine programme. 'We went over the back,' she said. 'By the burn. It's lovely over there, almost like being out in the country.'

For the first time that evening, Gordon turned to face her. 'Sometimes, I think you actually like living here,' he said. It was an accusation. He leaned forward. The veins in his neck were standing out. So she knew he was angry.

Rose said quickly, 'It's not that, Gordy. Its just that where you are – where we are – isn't the only thing. I mean – what we are – that counts for something too. That's more important in the end, isn't it?'

But Gordon didn't have time for existential questions like – who am I? As far as he was concerned, who you were wasn't the problem not when you were where they were. 'Look,' he said. 'Listen to me.' He knelt down before her and cupped her face in his hands. She got the feeling he was looking for forgiveness. He was so near she could feel his breath. He couldn't go on, he said. It was this place. He felt bad about her and the kid but there was nowhere to take them and he had to get out.

So now he'd said it. Rose began to cry.

She went for a bath. It wasn't all her fault, was it? A year, maybe two years of hard work and we'll be out of here. That's what they'd said. But the panic set in fast. Before the carpets were even laid, they were wondering if they'd make it back out again. The walls were newly plastered. So they had to wait six months before they could decorate and then they didn't bother because, as Gordon said, that would be like accepting they belonged here and this rathole was marked. You looked in the mirror and saw the place stamped all over your face. All the same, she would quite like to paint the walls. With a bit of imagination she could transform this place. Then, when they came in and shut the door, they might be able to forget about where they were.

The bath must have revived her. At two in the morning, Rose was restless. Even with the window open and just a sheet to cover her, it was too hot. Gordon was lying diagonally across the bed with one arm dangling over the side. He looked so peaceful now.

She got up, slipped on a robe and a pair of sandals and went out to the hall. The key was in the door. Rose unlocked it and stepped out onto the deck-access. The scheme looked like moon city at night. All those semicircles of light on the deck-access and fragile bridges in the sky, linking one crescent block to another. She felt like she was in a big, plastic bubble. The air smelt sharp and clean but fresh air wasn't natural in this artificial landscape. At night, it was easy to imagine she was inside some man-made dome with manufactured air and expensively imported damp-earth smells.

'Summertime and the living is easy' – Rose was humming as she walked along to the end of the block. She couldn't decide whether to go downstairs or cross the spindly bridge to the next block. It was possible to get from one end of the scheme to the other without going down to ground level. She stopped and leaned over the parapet. There was only so much that could be done to create an earth-like environment. The trees hadn't taken root too well up here. They looked gawky and out of place. Nothing was quite as it should be. All the same, she felt safe here. It was a self-contained, little colony and it was hard to imagine what lay outside.

She heard footsteps behind her. A man she knew vaguely by sight, stopped at the top of the stairs to catch his breath. 'Bloody inhuman, hen – these stairs. You realise if this building

had been one storey higher they would've had to give us a lift.'
Rose nodded politely. He came over and leaned on the parapet
next to her. He smelled of beer and perspiration.

'You ever seen the scale model of what this place is supposed to look like?' Rose shook her head. 'No – but I've heard
about it.' The original plans were often referred to like ru-
mours of paradise.

'All lies,' the man said. 'They never had the budget. Never
had any intentions. I was a brickie. Worked right here on the
site. Didnae think I would end up here, though.' The man
smiled grimly. In the moonlight his face shone with sweat. 'So
if you get the chance, hen – see if you get the chance to get out
of here don't waste it. This is no place to bring up a family.
Christ knows, you don't have to look too far to see how this
place is going.'

They both looked downstairs to the overspilling garbage
outside the bin area. Rose said nothing. It was a million miles
back to earth and the real world and if she ever got there it
would not be the way she remembered it.

Women's Writing And The Millennium

Liz Lochhead

'Women 2000' ... 'Approaching the Millennium' ... What does the future hold for women? for Scotland? for Scottish women?

(How should I know?)

What's so special about millennia anyway? Why should the digital, decimal countdown towards the Big Two and Three Zeroes encourage us to get a jildy on and shuck off the shackles of two thousand years of institutionalised 'Christian' misogyny? Aren't we already supposed to be in a 'Post-Feminist' situation? And what the hell is 'Post-Feminism' anyway? Is it, like, Post-Feminism as in Post-Modernism? A swing away from, even a rejection of the classical tenets of the movement? A time where the sacred-cow nature of its truisms demands a playful and ironic (if you like that sort of thing) stance? Or where decadent revisionists are currently indulging in a trivial, convoluted and baroque one (if you don't)?

Or could Post-Feminist mean 'after that time when gender-politics and the transparent justice of the arguments for change had become so much part of the agenda that the (male) media – and those females who identified with their self-interest – had long since retrenched and developed enough strategies, jokes, and putdowns to protect their own power against the onslaught?' Or does Post-Feminism simply imply

that crusading zeal has been rendered obsolete by the universal
acceptance at the deepest psychic level of absolute gender
equality? Is this already a truth self evident to every wee girl,
wee boy and grown up man and woman?

(I think not.)

You see the kind of crap I come out with when I try to write
this stuff? The way the words run away with themselves and
sloganise, their generality and abstraction making a sort of
noisy blur that sounds like it does, but doesn't mean anything.
And yet ... am I interested in these questions? Very. Especially:
what does the immediate future hold for Scottish women? But
I do not know the answer. Therefore I do not know what to
write.

I like to do it standing up.

What?

Well ... via the different voices of different characters to
build up a pastichy mosaic of a patchwork picture of how I see
things being at the present. Because if I had made some
statement of this, maybe I could develop some taste for
speculation about futures, utopian or otherwise?

Hell, I tell myself, relax, neither your task nor your talent is
for polemical or theoretical writing ... All right, I acknowledge
that reading those who can do it well – from Wollstonecraft to
Woolf to Carter to Rich to Mary Daly – has, variously, saved
my life, changed my thinking, informed my writing, helped me
to explain my feelings to myself. Nor do I feel that these
women are 'in history' in the sense of being in the past. Any
more than Atwood in her 'Survival' study of Canadian literature seems to be talking about another country ... No, the
truths these women tell seem to be almost universal. Why do
I feel I have nothing to add? I think my drive is towards
storytelling, recording voices, exploring ambivalences, trying

to be honest about the yes-and-no. You might think this a strange statement from someone who calls herself a poet and a playwright, but I think I have a sort of horror of self-expression. And it is self-expression that would be called for to write this essay. A statement of where I stood. And what attracts me is the shifting point, the caught voice, anything which momentarily illumines the ways of the heart, the life of the soul ... And, truthfully, I am just as interested in the complex or transparent strategies whereby individuals hide themselves from themselves, in the struggle to remain *un*-conscious) (given that consciousness predicates pain) as I am in the unduckable conflicts which reveal character. For me, in plays it's the *characters* (who I might not agree with or approve of, but must love with a love which goes beyond judgment); in poems it's the persona, the voice. A speculative essay leaves one nowhere to hide.

O K. Three points about being a woman writer in Scotland. One: your gender is not a 'problem'. Quite the reverse. The suppressed feminine inside all these males (and the suppressed feminine outside and inside of all these females) is crying out for sustenance and starving for soul-food. You have a territory to explore insufficiently mapped out or exploited. You have something to write about. The problem of getting them to admit you into their 'canon' is a very real one, but in a certain sense it's not your problem. Your job is to write it. Two: you don't *really* need 'role models'. At least not in the sense of 'a few women of my own age, class, geographical location, educational background, marital status and with same amount of children who also write historical novels/detective fiction/lyric poetry and validate the same subject matter and style as I fancy affecting.' Otherwise what's the point? There're writers you admire, male, female, dead, alive, posh,

plebeian, patrician, demotic. None of them found it easy ...
Read, enjoy, emulate, take to bits ... Three: you don't have to
'write positively about women' or create 'heroines'. To tell the
truth about things, even to delineate the chains of victimhood
is to write positively. ('Victim position number one is to refuse
to recognise that you're a victim.' Margaret Atwood in 'Survival'). You shouldn't be worrying about what you ought to
say about something 'as a woman'. Tell the truth and it'll be
from the woman's point of view, what are you going to do,
sprout a penis?

All very obvious stuff. But the kind of peptalk I need to give
myself all too frequently after twenty odd years at it. Pathetic
really.

Sometimes I ask myself whether Scotland (current major
export ersatz Glaswegian media-machismo) really is more
misogynist than the rest of U.K./ Western Europe? I doubt it.
What colour sexism in *your* country? ... But I don't doubt that
the traditional heavy industries of the central belt led to an
excessive gender-differentiation of roles. Nor that in the land
of the split personality, the home of the creators of *Confes-
sions of a Justified Sinner* and *Jekyll and Hyde* (mythmakers
more than novelists in these works) the male psyche is going to
fear the disintegration threatened by admitting further splits.
If Scottish male writers could do more than dimly sense
themselves as regarded as 'The Second nation', the 'Shadow',
the other, the outsider, the eccentric, the *anima*, almost (at
least from the point of view of the dominant London centre-of
the-empire literary establishment) then one might hope for
sympathy for the female position.

But it does not work like that ... Kicked dog looks for pussy
to bite. Inside this hunger exists though. You can see it in their
eyes ...

We've just got to burst their bloody canon by sheer volume and quality of what we say. That's my big hope for women and women's writing as we approach 2000.

Looking Forward to the Millennium
RONNIE MCDONALD

Looking towards the beginning of a new millennium fills me with an optimistic wonder. It's a little like standing on top of Ben Nevis, a dot on the landscape but with a spectacular view of all that I survey. After the reign of Thatcherism, the Pandora's box of all government, hope remains that succeeding generations, our daughters and sons, will do what we should have done.

There are so many different things I would hope women achieve in the future. But in an article like this, more must remain unsaid, unfortunately, than printed. Deliberately, I have concentrated on a few definable areas rather than the global issues of our century and next, such as world peace, the economic interdependence of the nations of Europe or what our world may be like in the Year 2000. But in looking forward, I am constantly aware of the wrongs of the present, the inequalities women continue to face daily.

I frequently become annoyed when listening to the equality debate. The concept, no matter the source represented, is always overwhelmingly supported. What bothers me about the debate is that for the majority of women in Scotland today, equality remains just that, a concept.

The decade 1979/1989 saw women's earnings as a percentage of male earnings rise by a mere 4.3% to 67.9%.

Legislation has had minimal effect on equalising pay. And this is paralleled by a hostility by employers to restructure pay and grading systems which continue to keep women in the lower earnings levels.

At the tail end of 1989, labour market commentators spoke excitedly about a demographic blip – of a shortage of young people for employment. Put only in economic terms, there was no thought of women having had some control of their own fertility. Yet the availability of contraceptive advice and facilities – wanted and campaigned for by women throughout this century – should be seen in broader economic terms. Put quite simply, without being able to control our fertility, we would not be able to be economically active.

That aside, the labour market suddenly needed women.

I think this need has come at a time when women need and demand to be recognised for what we contribute to the labour market. For years, we have been the invisible equation in the economy of our country. But too many barriers still prevent women from taking her equal role in employment. Most significantly is the lack of childcare provision, both pre-5 and out of school care.

Parenting and sharing are fine concepts, but in our world in the last decade of the 20th century, there are thousands of sole parents who can't share this concept. The majority are women, working in low paid, low status jobs. Without childcare support, job mobility and opportunity remain inaccessible.

Women's employment is clearly important to the economy of our nation. It is not, however, yet seen as being as important as men's employment. Employment analyses show that for many women their work is low-paid and low status. The same analyses also show that a substantial majority of women returners are, because of lack of childcare facilities, forced into jobs which neither match their skills or expertise. Such a mismatch of skills is a great loss to the economy and a disservice to the women returners. Tackling this must be a priority for both trade unions and employers. Training and retraining for women, the reverse side of the skills mismatch coin, must also be tackled seriously if women are to be properly and equally recognised in the labour market.

I would like to envisage a new millennium as a time when women achieve economic independence and equal employment opportunity.

Each generation hopes that succeeding generations will achieve more, will have a better quality of life. Education and communication help encourage young people to understand more about the world. But it is predominately a male view. I want women to be as visible in public life as men.

Women are not in government because of the problems of balancing domestic commitments with employment, and, perhaps more keenly, because government is seen as power – and so far men have jealously guarded this power. Since women got the vote , our representation in British national politics has hardly increased. In 70 years, only 139 individual women have sat in Parliament.

Scotland's record is quite awful. Parliamentary seats are seen as being reserved for men and while some political parties want to right this, years are bound to pass before any real progress could be made.

That's why I hope our daughters of the next century will be able to exercise their vote for equal representation, 50% women and 50% men, in the government of our country. A Scottish Parliament will not be truly representative of its nation unless women are able to sit equally alongside men in its democratic chambers.

The 1990s offer the people of Scotland the unique opportunity of deciding upon a new democracy, a Scottish Parliament. The Scottish Constitutional Convention is guiding the process. Women have already put forward their proposal for involving women in that government. Instead of issuing one ballot paper as we do now, two ballot papers would be available. One for male candidates and one for women candidates, all of whom would represent existing, serious political parties – or the entertaining Monster Loonies, etc.

Men and women would vote for the candidates of their choice in the electoral system eventually agreed by the people of Scotland. The net result would guarantee a government of 50% women and 50% men. It would not affect the ability of any political party to win an overall majority.

Equal representation of men and women – gender equality – might be regarded by some, by many, as too radical. But so too is a Scottish Parliament. Given the will, the recognition that women are equal with men, it is achievable.

As a woman trade union official in the 1980s and beginning of the 1990s, I am most recognisably in the minority. But as a woman worker, I am part of almost half the working population. It is widely acknowledged that the ability to influence change depends on the strength and commitment of those seeking change. It's also recognised that the degree of influence is keenly allied to the degree of participation, representation and extent to which one's views are considered. So like a Scottish Parliament, it is essential that women are represented and able to participate fully in our trade unions. Equally, trade unions must meet fully the needs of all its members, and women are vital to their future.

Women trade unionists have set an agenda of priorities over

the last two decades and more. Trade unions have been slow to respond, but the pace has now quickened, and many of the issues, previously considered as women's issues, such as health screening, childcare provision, abortion rights, domestic violence, are not marginalised but are mainstream campaigning and policy issues by trade unions.

I haven't been asked lately whether women's committees and women-only conferences should be abolished. But I have been asked why there aren't more women trade union officials. I ask the question too. The benefits would be significant in terms of how unions relate to the challenge of the 1990s and beyond, their image and their ability to recruit more women. In an economic climate of stagnation, where employers can engage two workers for the wage of one, trade unions must continue to positively discriminate on behalf of women. This means giving women more access, changing structures, and creating posts for women within these structures. By doing this, trade unions will be positive vehicles for change in a new century. Women trade unionists, so long the unequal partner, have gradually developed working links with women from local and national organisations. I hope that in the 21st century, these networks are strengthened by all trade unionists.

I was recently reminded of the statement displayed on the wall of US Federal Judge Ann Aldrich, 'women who aspire to be equal to men are under-achievers'. It's something to consider in the year 2000.

Midwives

ANNE MACLEOD

The maternity ward is always busy at midnight, with night feeds, squalling babies, and the midwives gathering. It's the time when nurses come round from the labour ward for a quick cup of coffee. They crowd into the small kitchen and share all their news, the latest joke, forecasts of the night's likely progress.

Harriet sees them as she passes, stiff and sore, walking as straight as her wound will let her. They are wide awake, (unlike Harriet,) happy and graceful in their white dresses and caps. Neat-waisted, all of them. Harriet still looks pregnant, though her baby was born two days ago. The nurse in charge of Harriet's ward looks round and smiles.

– Hi there. The little one settled? You practised mums have no bother at all. Would you like a drink? Hot chocolate?

Harriet accepts gratefully. It seems ages since she's eaten. She's only had fluids since the caesarean. The nurse nods.

– Fine. I'll bring it along for you. You get back to bed. It'll take a few minutes to boil the milk.

It's easier going back. She'd been a little dismayed to see how far it was to the bathroom, but the exercise has helped. She should have known it would. The thing is to get going and keep going.

Her little son sleeps soundly in his plastic crib, in cardboard-stiff hospital gown and blankets. He lies on his tummy, a small white mound with a fuzz of soft brown hair. He's a big baby – eight pounds – well, big for Harriet, but when she holds him, he feels small and light, like a doll. As she watches, he wriggles slightly, and a wrinkled hand creeps out to join the forehead. Harriet almost weeps. This is the tiny creature that spent so many weeks inside her, whose gentle movements she adored. She knew and loved him before his birth. She understands him already.

She eases herself into bed, taking her weight on her arms. She learned this trick last time, after painful experiment. It's amazing what you can do without abdominal muscles.

The door opens, and the midwife comes in with a cup of hot chocolate. She puts it on the locker, and asks,

– Can I get you anything else? Do you need some pain-killers?

– Yes, I think I probably do. I'm beginning to feel uncomfortable.

– Right. Just a second.

When Sheila, (that's the midwife) comes back, she slips round the bed to the baby. She smiles.

– He's super. And so good – well, quiet. It'll take you a wee while to find out if he's good.

Harriet laughs.

– Yes. It's all nonsense, isn't it? A noisy baby is just a noisy baby. How can they possibly be good or bad?

– Lots of people would disagree with you.

– You can't measure goodness in terms of crying. Anyway, I don't.

– Very wise. Good or bad, he's lovely.

– I think so. Harriet yawns.

A buzzer sounds in the ward. Sheila moves to the door and

pauses with her hand on the door-knob,

– We'll finish this discussion tomorrow. You'd better get some rest now. Goodnight.

– Goodnight. And thank-you.

Sheila slips out, and Harriet lies back carefully. She's exhausted. With luck she'll get two or three hours before he wakes.

As she drifts off to sleep, Harriet wonders why it's so easy to relax in such an unsympathetic environment. Her room is a small grey cell. They haven't painted it recently, because the new hospital will soon be open. There are holes in the floor where the trolley digs into the lino, and the walls are paper thin. You hear absolutely everything that goes on, like the wee lassie next door going into labour. (She hasn't come back from labour ward yet – she's been gone an awful long time.) But it's still easy to relax.

Easier than a hotel, for instance. When she went away from home by herself, not that it happened often, Harriet couldn't relax, found it difficult to sleep. But whenever her work or life circumstances take her into maternity wards, she's comfortable. Is it conditioning, or hormonal effect? She's read that institutionalised women, nuns and schoolgirls, tend to menstruate at the same time. Is that hormonal, or body-language? Perhaps it's factory farming, she thinks, drifting off to sleep. She dreams of battery chickens. The baby's high-pitched cry becomes the cock-crow to their clucking.

Harriet's parents wanted a boy when she was born, but that was just the remnant of a misguided cultural tendency. Why favour boy-children? We still do. Harriet's going to be cross at this, very cross. Not about her son, whom she adores; but at the smug way everyone assumes she wanted a boy 'this time', and with the flood of presents she receives after his birth. She didn't get that for either of her girls. And really she'd been hoping for another daughter, though the baby's wonderful, and she loves him anyway. She loves him for himself, not his sex.

When Harriet finally gets out of the chicken farm, her little chicken-licken is bawling for food. She rises stiffly and changes and feeds him. She changes him first, against all the advice in all the books, because she knows he'll yell whenever he's changed, and on a full belly too. Might as well get the yelling over all in one. She sits on the low, scruffy nursing chair, a lumpy pillow protecting her wound; the baby, on top, sucks away for all he's worth. Her nipples are sore, and it's nearly five o'clock. It's been a good night, really.

Just as she puts him down, Sheila comes back in to check her pulse and blood pressure, and to look at her wound. They're all fine.

— I thought I'd nip along for a bath, says Harriet.

— A shower might be easier.

— I'll be careful getting in and out, she promises.

— I'm speaking to an expert, of course. I forgot. Okay, off you go.

— He still looks very peaceful. Hasn't he woken yet?

— He was screaming blue murder a minute ago.

Harriet stands up slowly, moves stiffly to the sink to get her towel and wash-bag.

— Could I possibly have some paracetamol?

— Certainly.

Sheila disappears behind the door, and returns with the tablets in a plastic cup.

— Are you sure these are strong enough?

— They're fine if you take them regularly. Distalgesic gives me bad dreams. I'd rather have the stiffness than the nightmares. Sheila, what did the wee lass next door have?

Sheila's face falls slightly.

– She's still in labour ward.

– I'm sorry. I didn't mean to put you on the spot. I know you can't discuss the other patients. I'm off for that bath now, before I seize up altogether. And Harriet starts the long trek to the bathroom, which seems shorter than it did the day before. Progress.

The bath is deep and hot. She kneels, not in religious fervour, but because she'll find it easier to rise from this position; today at any rate. But it is conducive to thought. Perhaps those nuns have something after all. She shakes her head. Nuns in a maternity ward? That's Freudian. She knew a nun at school, long and thin, sharp as a razor.

In those days, Harriet wanted to be a nun, because she liked the long skirt, and the rosary at the waist. She liked the coif. She wasn't sure about shaving her hair off, but anyway Sister Edward had hair. It stuck out the back of her cap. So they didn't all shave their heads, or not La Sagesse nuns anyway. There must have been some wisdom in the order. But it was funny to be called Sister Edward, a contradiction in terms.

Harriet often used to ask out of class when she didn't really need to go to the toilet, just so that she could trip downstairs, holding her pretend-nun skirt, bow her pretend-nun knee at the statue on the stair, and run across the playground, as if in a habit. Sister Edward must have killed herself laughing. If she saw.

She'd probably laugh to see me now, thinks Harriet, kneeling in the water, like a burst balloon with stitches, eyes heavy with lack of sleep. And yet she's happier than she's been for months.

Why? Is it the joy of motherhood, oft, yes, oft quoted by

male poets and the like? Is it just that she's in the post-natal maelstrom, and hasn't yet reached the bubbling stage? To be honest, yes, but she's too tired to bother with details like that.

Harriet thinks, as she kneels in her bath, that the nurses get kinder and kinder. More human. This time, they're all on first name terms. They take great trouble to get to know you; they mean it too. It can't be easy. They have such a range of people to deal with, from the wee lassie next door, unmarried, Harriet thinks, though no-one's actually said that – and she's worried about that wee girl, she should have been back by now – to her, Harriet, ageing medical secretary, who still looks nine months pregnant on her third post-operative day.

And they've all their own problems to cope with, thinks Harriet. She knows that Sheila's divorced, and childless. She was unable to conceive, and that put a terrible strain on her marriage. But it didn't stop her enjoying, and excelling at her profession. Of the other nurses, Mary is also divorced, with one child. She would have liked more, she says. Maggie's newly married, and not long qualified, but very kind. When Harriet bursts into tears later in the day, she'll be very helpful. So will Myra, recently widowed. Her selflessness will make Harriet cry all the more. But she doesn't know this yet, and the bath is getting cold. She rises slowly, and reaches for her towel.

Harriet makes a point of putting her make-up on in hospital. She does this every day, as early as possible, because she doesn't know who will drift in to visit. Hospital friends often drop in before nine.

David won't come till evening, and then the girls will be with him, which is probably best. He's been very quiet since the birth, though Harriet can tell he's pleased to have a son. Stupid, really. If it had been a girl, he'd probably be off with that woman by now. No. She stops herself. She can't be objective about that. He says there's nothing in it. That may be the truth.

It is true, actually. Well, half-true. David was tempted, but didn't have the gumption to reach his objective, though he could perhaps have done it. Perhaps. But his guilty anger does nothing for Harriet. He is pleased about the boy, wants her to stay at home with the baby. This doesn't figure in Harriet's plans. She needs her work, and she's good at it. She needs the family too.

– Papers! Papers!

The call echoes through the early morning corridor. The nurses are nowhere to be seen, closeted in the office, probably, giving the report. Harriet struggles along the corridor to the end of the queue. She feels old and insecure. Her wound feels tight.

A hospital acquaintance passes and smiles brightly.

– My, you're looking sprightly! When was the section?

– Monday.

– You're doing very well.

Momentarily, she stands taller, feels brighter. On her way back, she thinks that sprightly is a rather aged adjective. She sags. Her nipples hurt. She gives in and asks the nurse for an antiseptic spray.

– Haven't you tried marigold ointment? asks Maggie, as she hands it over.

– It's supposed to be very effective. Ask your husband to get some. If he can't, I'll get it for you tonight.

The day slips by. Harriet reads the paper from cover to cover. There's a long article – *Where Does Mother Go Now?* A feminist view of motherhood, or a changing perspective of feminism, Harriet can't decide which, nor could the journalist. In another story, a self-designated 'failed' feminist describes her early days with a brand new baby. Harriet thinks of her own first go at motherhood. It was terrifying. She got better with practice. David didn't, but then he didn't practise.

Changing attitudes are inevitable, thinks Harriet. You can't blame people for being surprised that motherhood is difficult when it's written off as easy, instinctive. Unskilled. Too much so-called women's work is written off that way, children, housework, cooking. And yet that isn't all of life, by no means. These tasks are all important, but not female preserves. Or they didn't need to be. Family work. Family work needs family participation. Equal division of labour, in and out of the home.

She sighs. That isn't possible for child-birth, but rearing of the children could be shared, to everybody's benefit. For herself, Harriet's quite sure she'll be happier, and best achieve all her roles – mother, housewife, self – while working in the home and out of it. She'll come home with enthusiasm. It will be a pleasure to return to her daughters, her little son, her husband. And anyway, she thinks, they'll have us all back at work, all the married women, like it or not. Population problems. Expedience.

On the ward notice-board there's a poster for Radical Midwives, something to do with natural child-birth, she thinks. She doesn't know. But it sounds good. Strong. Harriet feels strong.

She feels strong. And radical.

Walking Back

ALISON MILLAR

'I wouldn't go out there, Madam, if I was you.'

'Oh Tom! Don't be so dismal!'

I am standing in the foyer of my apartment block, trying to get out.

Tom blocks my way. Tom is one of our Security Service men, and he's assigned to be my personal protector. He used to be in the Police Force before it was disbanded, and he's kept the policeman's air of stolid immoveability. He's built like a bouncer too – I don't think anything could shift him unless he wanted to move. Nevertheless he is human – he adores me. I rather like him, too.

'Madam – my instructions from Mr. Faisal are … '

I cut in. 'Mr. Faisal needn't know.'

I can glimpse the outside world beyond Tom. It's a spring day, but spring is mean this year. The sky is overcast, and there's a half-hearted wind blowing drizzle and bits of paper past the door. It isn't the best day for a walk, but I need to go. Being loved and possessed by a rich man sometimes gives me claustrophobia.

Tom is quietly considering what I have just said. He disapproves of my insubordination, that's clear, but can he resist it? I tap my heels on the floor and they make a brittle clicking noise. It signals that I'm ready to go. Don't keep the lady waiting, Tom.

He works out a solution. I'll have to come with you,' he tells me. Oh very good Tom. Haven't you the wit to realise that I'm going out *because* I want to be rid of you, and the apartment, and Mr. Faisal, just for a little while? But I can't *tell* him any of this.

'Are you ready to go, Madam?' he asks deferentially.

I have been ready for over five minutes. I hurry outside, much too abruptly for my heels, and I start to totter like some drunken slut chasing a man. That WILL NOT DO, but it's so easy to lapse, it's frightening. I regain control and walk the few remaining steps to the pavement, as if the whole world were watching me manage my shoes. Once on the pavement, I survey the road. Besides Tom and myself there is a solitary woman, walking away from us. The bitch is wearing a fur coat; I could rip it off her back and drape it onto mine. I love the thought of wearing fur, but I can't wear it. As a director of CareChem, Mr. Faisal cannot be seen to support the fur trade.

CareChem household products are never tested on animals – I swear this is true, although I don't know what they use instead. The public buy their compassion when they buy CareChem bleach. If Mr. Faisal bought me fur, the compassion would lose its market value instantly. Nobody's told me all this – I've worked it out. I'm not stupid.

Tom is at my side and is offering me a cigarette. I refuse. Nobody who is anybody smokes – at least, not in public. But on the rubbish tip, on the other side of the fence we've built to protect ourselves, they kill for fags.

'Where to, Madam?' poor rebuffed Tom asks.

'The park.' I add, my voice tailing off, 'the one near the fence ... ' I try to sound casual, as if where it is, is unimportant. But that's its attraction. I want to come up against the limits of my life now, even though I know I won't step over them. It's a way of living dangerously that isn't dangerous at all.

'It's very dangerous, Madam,' Tom chimes in, 'at the present time. There is a – a male person around that's come in from the dump. He was reported to our men about three hours ago. We're looking hard, and we hope to find him soon.'

And when you do, you'll kick the poor bastard to death because he's lower than you are. Like you were killing a rat. The people outside our fence are vermin, they're excrement. They stink. They haven't any money because they can't or won't or don't work. The State used to give them cash to live on, but it doesn't anymore. So they live outside the fence we've built and exist on our rubbish. It's easy to descend to that level, but it's as hard as hell to pull yourself out of it. The most help with your life you'll get is from the charity nurse, who'll delouse you and give you a course of food supplement tablets.

It is not a very long walk to the fence from the apartment building, and as we approach we can smell the garbage. It isn't very strong today but it still makes me want to retch. The Security Service people assigned to guard the fence have a horrible job. No wonder they want to kill the people they're employed to keep out.

We have to walk about a hundred metres alongside the fence before we turn away into the park. I reach into my handbag, pull out a perfume-soaked handkerchief and hold it over my nose and mouth. This is becoming a standard gesture for ladies, when they have to go near the fence, and is sometimes affected by men, too. As we walk along, Tom shouts a greeting to a few of the Security Service personnel. I think he is flaunting me, and his cushy job. They reply with a nod or a laugh. 'You lucky ... ', the laugh says.

They would never dare to say it openly because they are

subcontracted to CareChem, and know I belong to their boss.

We reach the park. It is bounded by low black railings and a wall of ancient trees, which, when the leaves are out in summer, looks impenetrable. We are joining the park at the playing fields, but this is not where we'll stay. My goal is the labyrinthine growth of shrubbery ahead where, hopefully, I'll lose Tom. But first I need his consent. 'Tom,' I begin, 'that man who got through the fence – where do you think he'll be by now?'

Tom is delighted that I ask his opinion. 'Well … they head for the city, to look for anything worth stealing. That's where he'll be.'

'So I should be quite safe here?'

'From him, yes.'

This is where I push my luck. 'If it's safe, perhaps I could spend some time alone here for a little while.' I wheedle. 'Please, Tom.'

'Madam, my duties are … '

I don't want to get tough, but I'll have to. 'Tom. if you don't let me go, Mr. Faisal will find out that you tried to screw me in the park.' He is frightened now. I've won, but it isn't much of a victory. People like Tom annoy me sometimes, with their uniforms stuffed full of somebody else's authority. Turn that authority against them, and they're helpless. No brains, no backbone. I turn to go, without arranging a time to meet him again. He must know that he's beneath my consideration.

I'm free! No more Tom, no more Mr. Faisal … I don't want to think about the time when I'll have to rejoin them. Over there is the shrubbery, where I can hide and get back to being the person I've buried, who I never thought I'd miss. I start to run towards the shrubbery, as fast as my heels will take me.

As I turn a corner, I crash. I stumble into a hollow, lurch and fall off my high heels. I lie, spread over path and soil, tights ripped, dress stained, hands black and bloody. My handbag has landed ahead of me, open, with its contents scattered. As I stare at it, I see a figure worm its way out from a nearby bush. It's a man, with all the marks of the rubbish tip upon him – the rotting rags, the dirt and the unmistakeable stench of garbage and unwashed body. Revolting. So much for Tom's prediction. The man shouldn't have broken cover, but my bag must have been too much of a temptation. He must think I'm unconscious, otherwise surely he wouldn't dare. He can have whatever money he can find. I'm not going to cause a fuss and give Security Service their prize, just for a few pounds.

He finds a note and some coins and stuffs them into his trouser pocket. Then he takes something I didn't think he'd be interested in. It's a small newspaper photograph of a baby – a child born on the tip – being held by its father. The photograph is yellow – it's about five years old – but I only found it recently in a stack of papers. I'll be damned if I'll part with it.

I raise myself up, just as the man is about to hide back in the bush. 'Stop!' I command, clear, but not loud. The man turns and stares at me in terror, then tries to dive for cover. I lunge forward, and stop him by grabbing his wrists. He doesn't fight. He's weak – in fact he's had it. There's no life in him – he's just existing until he dies. This always happens, and it happens early. Boys from the tip are fighters – they have to be, to live into their teens. They're angry, they're horny … and they're old men at twenty-one. They grow old when they realize it's pointless fighting because they'll never win. Then the drink takes them, or the drugs. Or simply, life. This man could be anything between twenty-five and sixty. It's impossible to tell.

I'm almost sick with disgust from touching him, so I squeeze his wrists tightly – clamping him in – in case I lose control. In

return his fingers let the photograph fall onto the muddy
ground. 'If you don't give me that picture now,' I state quietly,
'I will hand you over to Security Service.' It's an unreasonable
demand when I'm holding his wrists, and I suppose I could
pick it up myself. But something inside me that knows I'm
richer and more powerful than he will ever be, makes me
vicious. I look down on him and he stares up at me. Tears are
dribbling from his little shrunken eyes. I hate to see a man cry,
even a broken-down wreck of a man like this one. I say more
softly, 'If you give it to me now, there'll be no trouble.'

He lowers his head again, and looks at the picture on the
ground. He mutters something like 'dead. 'S dead.'

People on the tip are developing their own way of speaking,
that hardly involves speech at all, just the most important
words of a message. Outsiders normally find it very difficult to
understand, but this seems fairly clear to me. I try it out.
'Dead? Who's dead?'

'Her.'

'Her? In the picture?' He seems to nod. This won't be real
unless I find out more. 'Is the baby in the photograph dead?
How do you know?'

He does not, or cannot, answer. I am firing too many
questions at him, demanding too many words. He looks ahead
blankly, those old tears still wet on his dirty cheeks. I try to
reach him by a different route. 'What about the mother – does
she know?'

'She don't know … She come here … ' He scuffs the ground
with his foot. 'Bitch!'

My God. He hates that woman. I hope he isn't bright
enough to wonder what I'm doing with the photograph. But he
can't be the man I … He doesn't look like the man in the
picture. But I've changed too, and it's *my* change, not his, that

makes us disgust and fear each other. I don't want to give him his name because this isn't the person I remember. And it might not be him at all. If not, it can't be my child. I can't ask the child's age, because people on the tip don't think in years and time anymore. I release the man's wrists – he won't run away – and hold one of my hands at about the height of a small five-year-old child.

'Was she this high?' He barely nods, again.

I'm pushing us on, punishing us both, but I need to know more before I can believe what I'm thinking. How did she die? Why? He has to tell me – and tell me fast. Tom's coming. 'Tell … how … ?' I slip into the way they speak, not questioning, but prompting. The story he gives is devastating.

He tells me that the CareChem people came and offered him five pounds for his daughter. She was to be used to test a new product – they didn't say what. They came back and told me she'd died. Killed by an overdose. They said it was accidental.

I'm guilty, with Mr. Faisal, and Tom and my scented handkerchief, just as much as those people in white coats who administer death in the laboratories. I killed her just as much as they did. And the worst of it is, that now I know, I can't weep for her. She's still just that picture from the newspaper. Not real at all.

Tom's approaching footsteps save me from thinking. When he comes round the corner he will find me, as he would put it, in some distress. He will take out his revenge on his position in life by kicking to death the man hiding in the bushes. And I will point the way.

I will do this because it's right and proper that Tom should protect me from my assailant. I have a lot to lose if I were found to be protecting *him*. I will also do this because I can't join the man in grieving. He's had enough of life and sadness

– I can at least allow Tom to take it from him. It is the best way out for both of us.

When Tom has finished, there will be nothing left to cry over, not even the photograph. But then my tears will start, and it will be a long time before they stop. This outcome is the only way I can let myself grieve. I will be crying over the part I played. I will be crying for myself.

Extracts from *Among You Taking Notes*

NAOMI MITCHISON

Naomi Mitchison's prodigious output as a writer embraces novels, short stories, poetry, plays, autobiography, various kinds of non-fiction, and books for children. Her fiction ranges from social realism to historical myth and science fiction, where a sympathetic imagination enters deeply into the dilemmas of many societies dead and unborn. An English-educated Scottish socialist from the intellectual aristocracy, who has travelled widely in Europe and the Third World, she has fought hard for many causes during a long life. Among them, feminism has always been important to her and she has sometimes believed it to be true bedrock, as can be seen below.

On the outbreak of war in 1939, soon after settling at Carradale in Kintyre, she began keeping a diary as part of the Mass Observation programme. These extracts from an edited version of this, published in 1985 under the title *Among You Taking Notes*, show some of the vivid random outcroppings of her varied concern for the condition of women, as it was brought to mind by the daily life of the house, farm and village in wartime. In this they perhaps capture the immediate flavour of the time and the writer's own personality, and also reflect the ways in which most women with other demands on them are forced to do their thinking about issues of gender, better than a more formal and systematic treatment could do.

22 December 1941

L. was looking tired and depressed; we both tried to cheer her up, but I'm afraid she is a bit gloomy about this quarrel between me and D.M.; she brought me over a note from him. I don't think he sees my point very much, however it will no doubt clear itself up. I think it all means that my feminism is deeper in me than, say, nationalism or socialism: it is more irrational, harder to argue about, nearer the hurting core. I can write about it, from angles, and have, in *We Have Been Warned, The Home* and others, but unless people have the same experience, it doesn't get across to them. D.M. thinks he sticks up for women, but of course it isn't the same thing, nor can it be until the economic side is cleared up. I sometimes think that I could work my heart out for people here, but yet they wouldn't really think as much of me as of D., because they know it isn't me who has the money.

Friday 14 February 1941

…I asked what he [J. W.] thought of communal meals, he said he didn't hold with them, the only kind he wanted were big kitchens for a street, where women could go and cook; I said that wouldn't release the women. He said what for? To work in factories? I said to do all [or] anything they want to. He said if she has a nice home and a good wage and plenty to eat that's what a woman wants. We then went for one another, and his girl sat silently eating and looking blank. God knows, she wouldn't want anything else. His theory is that you can't alter human nature, not love and family life. I said what about birth control? He said, Surely you don't hold with that, Mrs Mitchison? I very nearly savaged them both, but kept my temper sufficiently to suggest that part of Communism was to get people out of the enclosing walls of the home, to get them to see things, not individually but socially, to get them not to compete, but to co-operate. I said that it was possible for people to regard even their own families as respect-worthy individuals, not as objects of ownership. But of course it was no good. He just thinks I'm balmy, and that of course no real woman would believe any of that nonsense. He says of course if you'd ever been a working class wife… Very odd, it's really this kind of thing that makes me furious. The common working class attitude, when the girls are expected to do the domestic chores, the women must even spend their evenings sewing and mending while the men have a paper or a game. It makes me feel murderous. And it can't be changed in a generation. Mrs W. agrees with me, says Yorkshire men are all like that. They all really treat their women as dirt, they don't understand that you don't want to be cooking and washing all day. But it's bothering when the younger generation are worse than the old.

Wednesday 21 January 1942
Wild storm, snow everywhere, I slept in, would have slept longer but Bella had to see me about housekeeping. Stayed in bed half morning and read Eric Gill's *Autobiography*…*

Curiously unaware of certain things old Gill was! I agree with so much, it's what I'm after myself. Smashing the idea that art is an expression of the artist's self and all that balls, that it is service. After all what is this book of mine going to be but service to Scotland, or rather, to the dumb Scots, the ones who need to be given pride and assurance and kindness, that's why I read it with such care to D. M., why his opinion matters

---

*Eric Gill is an artist best known for his sculpture, type design and his fine engravings and woodcuts many of which are explicitly erotic. Gill died at the age of 58 in 1940 shortly before the publication of his autobiography.

to me why indeed I need it in order to get on. He's the
prototype, the image, one I've got to bring alive. But would old
Gill admit that a woman can make a work of art at all? He
doesn't. All his art adventures are between young men. The
women are *there* certainly, very important, but in a world of
their own, the world of conversation, of the house and farm
and all; I see the point. I have that world. I know it matters. It
matters like hell, that's why I think my farming and all that is
important, I'm not just a potato factory. But also I'm an artist,
I'm aware. I'm an adventurer. Like him, too, I know that
discipline is necessary, though I don't accept his variety of
discipline, probably because I am more intelligent than he was
– not a better artist, but just more intellectual, a better I.Q., the
hell of an intellectual heredity. I can think past him. He just
hasn't faced certain things, especially science. He has run
away. You can't do that.

But he talks about 'his' women, his family, his three daughters. I wonder what they really thought of it, or if they were just
swept away by him, as one undoubtedly might be, would be if
one wasn't very tough. And he doesn't know about them. He
says 'I do not gather that women have, in general, much of an
eye for the beauty of their lovers' bodies… They are not
inflamed by images…they do not make or go to see or buy
pictures of men as men do pictures of women.' The hell he
thinks that. The important word is 'buy'. Women haven't had
the money and, until a few more can buy, the rest will be
ashamed. They can be made more uncomfortable by censure
than me. I remember awfully badly wanting to buy Gill's own
wood engraving of Mellors in *Lady Chatterley's Lover* for
exactly these reasons. He was a naked man, with all the Gill
emphasis on the penis. But at the time I hadn't the money. It
was five guineas. I never seemed to have any money. I was

always lending it to people or getting extra things for the children or something; Goodness knows I had more, earned and unearned, than most women. Also I had a conscience about spending it on myself and this would obviously have been *for* myself. The only thing I haven't had a conscience about buying for myself is books. Which accounts for the general overflow of books.

And as to being inflamed by images – ! The interstices of my days are full of erotic images. Quite often, of course, I use them as current to turn the mills of the imagination. I am 44 and should know what I'm doing by now. I can think clearly and unresentfully of my lovers in the past, certainly of their naked bodies. I should suppose that most women thought rather more in terms of touch and less in terms of vision than men (or conceivably a writer thinks more in such terms than a sculptor). I think also a lot in terms of smell. I can remember the smell of the neck of a man whom I haven't seen since we said goodbye in 1934 – I was reminded of him just now through seeing his name as a lecturer. Here the interstices of work and thought are filled with the erotic images of the men I see and admire and work with: not, alas, their naked images, as they mostly wear three layers of jerseys, but their laughter, their eyes and mouths, touch of their lips and fingers, smell of them most of all. So long as I think of them without resentment and anger and possessiveness I know there's nothing wrong. I hope they think of me with the same vividness and love, the same admission that it's sexual and the same absence of guilt. The latter is the difficulty. So long as the convention is to think of these things guiltily, then people will make a mess of them. I don't think it wrong in any man that I love to have erotic images of other women. But if the other women think it is, if they think that we must only imagine in couples, then there's the devil to pay. They go back to Mark 'Whosoever looketh on a woman to lust after her hath committed adultery with her already in his heart. If thy right eye offend thee, pluck it out…' Of course, that means you 'lust', not just take the surface meaning, as interpreted by Banu Israel and by generations of owners, of possessors, of those for whom a wife was a tool, a thing of their own, a breeder, for whom love between man and woman was a wrong thing except in the regularised and commercial relationships, for whom that [relationship] was threatened by the stranger. If you 'coveted' your neighbour's wife (and D. put down coveting for C. when we had Sins as one of our 'Categories' the other night) you obviously wanted to own her. That's the wrong thing. That's the catch every time. Ownership. If I 'covet' X or Y or Z here at Carradale, as indeed I do, it's not because I want to own them or to get anything out of them or to exploit them or their families in any way; I just simply like them; I like their shapes, I like their eyes, their smiles, they way they have of speaking or laughing; I want, as it were, not just a slip, not a tease, but the whole thing. Yet I know that if I were to take it, it would be misinterpreted, probably by them, certainly by anyone connected with them. I don't suppose they would go as far as to think out the implications of their condemnation, they wouldn't say to themselves, we condemn her because she is taking something that belongs to someone else; they would just condemn me plain, say I was a whore and leave it at that. And because I am doing work here, trying to give people other ideas of human relationships, starting with the simplest form of it, my own relations, first towards my family, then towards my friends, I mustn't jeopardise that. If they do condemn me in one thing they will condemn me in everything. And I couldn't blame them considering their historical conditioning and this god-awful church that thinks of sex as sin.

It is much more important that I should be able to change people's minds about one another in this other way, to try to show them non-possessive, generous human relations in other ways. if I can do that, the other thing will follow in time, in a hundred years, say. It is always a bore being ahead of one's time, and coming up here I move back fifty years from, say, London or Birmingham (though equally I move to a world where they still *can* understand generous relationships, where it hasn't all been killed by industrialism). Again, if I were to have love affairs, that would countenance other people in having them who might quite well not be disciplined about it at all, might allow them to wreck families, or might easily let the possessive motive creep in. There is of course much more of that in a society where the women have no money of their own and only get it from men, and their only saleable asset is their bodies. I hope it may help them a bit, being wage earners, forestry girls and so on.

Well let's hope nobody reads this who won't try to understand it...

Sunday 12 August 1945

... the girls and I and J. discussing this business of babies. It really is doing in both J. and to a lesser extent R. And the same thing has happened to me. I can no longer concentrate myself, feel I ought to be doing something else, at any rate I ought to be in half an hour. One is listening for the telephone or for a child. Even if I want to join in a conversation I feel myself impelled to distract myself, not to give full concentration, to read a book at the same time. I *can't* now think in a pointed way about *anything*. I can rather more easily concentrate when writing. But it is rare to have an hour undistracted.

Because of this I know I can never be first class at anything. The mornings are slightly better, but are more occupied by other things. By the evening I am too tired to do anything. I cannot even read a serious book now. R. may escape because her job is itself more separate. For J. and me – there, now I've had ten minutes in the kitchen dealing with a joint that has had the flies on it, one gets the maggots off with vinegar and then it's perfectly all right, but no town person can do it – for J. and me, our lives are part of our work. The poetic ideas bud all the time and either live or die. J. was saying that constantly things and situations were shaping into poems or stories but they never got written down. I'm the same, but at least when I was young I learnt to work fast, to type at a professional rate, to write on scraps of paper *anywhere*, to be fairly ruthless. But not enough. We are both of us full of ideas and images and all the gestalt of writing and it may be pigeon-holed for ever, it may never be dealt with for the future as such things should be. What we might do is lost except in so far as we can pass it on to our children in our chromosomes. The fact that our children are voluntarily begotten makes it all the more difficult. We cannot just say they are something that has happened to us, an act of God or however it should be expressed. We deliberately took on this burden. Yet we didn't know beforehand how crippling it would be. R. thought she could combine her work as a doctor with having children. But she may yet be able to. I am more doubtful about J. She is almost deliberately sacrificing herself now.

Liberation and the Vest

WILMA MURRAY

It is a theory of mine that you can close-guess a woman's age by her attitudes to underwear, and in particular her reaction to the subject of vests.

Quietly running a parallel course to the history of women's liberation, it seems to me, runs the history of the vest as an article of women's clothing. Women of the generation before me still wear full length interlocked-cotton vests (though where they buy them is a small mystery); my generation – the war babies – is the one which shed its vests under the critical eyes of mothers; my daughter's generation wouldn't be seen dead in them and it is entirely possible that her daughter will need to have the garment explained in the way I have often tried and failed to explain what a Liberty Bodice is, or was. A training corset?

I am talking serious, prototype vests here, of course, not the dinky little waist-hugging numbers which masquerade under the name these days, all pretty with lace and shapely with Lycra, even in the thermal mode. The vest I knew was a garment which never looked good even in the packet. Even sleek models in glossy mail order catalogues failed to glamorise these garments but just stood around in silly Grecian postures, looking faintly embarrassed. No, my vest was a shapeless white cotton tube which reached right down over

your bum, or, if you were unlucky and small like me, halfway
to your knees. Within minutes, it had worked itself up into a
lump under your knickers and by the end of the day had
stretched, bagged, crumpled and creased every which way so
that, empty, it lay there like some weird, deflating, deformed
torso.

I can remember exactly when I finally discarded these vests
forever. I was fourteen and had just fought the fight to have a
bra, which, I was led to believe, should be worn over the vest.
This lumpy combination was not at all pleasing to my developing self-image and I rebelled and left my vest off for the
school Christmas party in December 1953. I can still recall the
sinful, luxurious feel of pink satin against my skin as I went out
of the door. Never mind that circular-stitched bras were all the
rage at the time and I probably looked as though I had two ice-
cream cones under my dress, I was armed by that feeling
against the dire warnings that I would catch my death, probably, without something warm next to my skin.

At that time, I believed that vests were worn for their
warmth and to a certain extent that made sense in times when
bedrooms were seldom heated, so that the vest was often worn
in bed as well. It was therefore the one garment which never
came off, except to put on a clean one or to have a bath. In
other words, it covered your naked – oh, wicked, wicked word
– body. Taking off your vest, then, must have been loaded with
connotations well beyond my fourteen-year-old imagination
and I now understand that on that December night I was being
warned more about catching sex than catching my death of
cold. For vest, then, read chastity belt. Anyone who has stood
in front of a full length mirror in a tight newly washed vest, as
I have done, will testify to the fact that it serves much the same
function, at least psychologically.

When I think back, I realise that at about the same time, my mother's generation was just at the stage of discarding boned and laced corsets. New fibres were allowing for corsets to lose their ability to stand up by themselves when taken off at night, and to have an elasticity and softness which took that generation a long time to accept. My mother was hard to convince that these garments would control the flab quite as well as the old scaffolding. They even came in wicked colours, like white and black, and not just that shade of salmon pink I will associate with corsets for the rest of my life. I had watched my mother putting on those old instruments of torture, or even more vividly, diving into the bedroom after a dance to get shot of them even before she took her shoes off. So I was glad that by the time it was suggested that I need some sort of control – you reached puberty and somehow everybody was speaking about control – there were little elastic girdles which I could pull on over my knickers. All that these garments really succeeded in doing was to redistribute the flab, up or down, resulting in bulges above, or bulges below, depending on your original shape. I was bulges above. Also, a new generation was seduced into giving up the control of their stomach muscles to the miracle fibres built into these grotesque little garments.

This, of course, was in the days before tights, so these girdles had suspenders hanging down at four points around the thighs, and there was a whole youth sub-culture developed round how to disguise the inevitable bumps when you were sitting down,(which included wearing the girdle outside in) and people of my age will also know exactly what to do in the event of one of the suspender bobbles breaking off and getting lost.

Later, tights and panti-girdles banished forever the misery of sitting, unexpectedly, on a suspender stud and having to wriggle yourself free discreetly when in company. They also split the young female world in half – those who wore their tights *over* and those who wore their tights *under*. I am an under.

So my mother had got rid of corsets, I got rid of vests and by the time I was a mother, the Woodstock generation was getting rid of bras and there wasn't a vest in sight. That bra-burning symbolism of the women's liberation movement was very powerful. It was the control business again – one generation defying the previous one by abandoning one of the symbols of control. As it happened, anatomy and gravity militated against my considering that move, however liberated, and I confess I found myself looking at the new generation of bra-less young and wondering, much as my mother did before me, no doubt, if it was really quite wise and whether it might not all end in tears. Getting a first bra (a trainer bra, no less) seemed set to change its significance entirely to become the symbol of giving up, when the boobs no longer stood up to being bounced around under a teeshirt. The bra, like the vest before it, seemed destined to become a symbol of old age. I could see a new generation of daughters turning round to the mothers and suggesting it was time the old boobs were under control, and the oldies having to go sneaking into funny little old fashioned draper shops in small towns asking for bras and being served by even older, but sympathetic, staff who understood.

The legacy of those heady days is choice. Bras are entirely optional these days. Now it looks as if tights are going out of favour with the young. It's all bare legs or natty little socks these days. Logically, then, the next garment to go must be knickers or whatever the present term is – knickers is too big a word for so small a garment. It could well have happened already, for all I know. I may have to wait for grandchildren to grow up to confirm my suspicions. But a recent TV advert shows a young woman coming out of the shower, putting on deodorant and then slipping into a black dress and high heels. Underwear by ——, the advert tells us. The name is the name of the deodorant. So perhaps the skin age has already arrived for some.

Looking to the millennium, then, I would predict that those under the age of thirty will probably wear no underwear at all or else, history having this habit of repeating itself, the fashion will be for huge bloomers, petticoats and laced corsets – but not quite the kind my mother wore. The difference will be that this time, like all the slippery, satiny, pretty, skimpy things on open display in the most respectable of shop windows, they will definitely be meant to be seen.

Elderly woman in street to husband, quote: 'Oh, my goodness, that's not decent. Malcolm, just don't look, now. They haven't even got vests on. Malcolm!'

I can, however, confidently forecast that the vest as I knew it and my mother knew it and my grandmother knew it, will *never* ever come back into fashion, even if we were to enter another ice age.

Parable

Tessa Ransford

The tree longed for the day
when she could cease bearing fruit.

Year after year all her energies
went into fruit production.

It was as if root and branch,
stem, bud, leaf and flower

had no other talent or potential
than toiling to make fruit –

the burden of it, the weight,
and the never-ending labour.

'If only', thought the tree,
'I could use my roots to study something in
depth,

my leaves to be creative
in other ways: dance, music, poetry.

I wish I could exist for my own sake
and play my full part in global ecology.'

At last the time came
when the tree was no longer fruitful.

She shuddered with terrible ecstasy,
knew herself essential and beautiful.

Autumn came. The tree was lightsome,
shed a profusion of brilliant ideas.

But the farmer was no fool:
'useless', he decided, and felled her.

Women of the 90s

Myrtle Simpson

… My claim to sporting fame is due to a failure. Three of us set off to ski to the North Pole. We wanted to prove that we could reach it unsupported. It was twilight as a little plane left us on the most northerly point of land in the Americas. It looked as if the sun would come over the horizon any minute, but we knew that in fact it would not return till mid March, six weeks away. It was perishing cold … -54°. We loaded food and camping gear for our 400 mile journey onto the one sledge and hauled on our harnesses … no dogs to do the work for us! We were totally alone. The cold ate into our hearts, sapping our strength, as we inched our way forward. Close to the land, the frozen sea was a chaos of vast blocks of ice. We picked our way through as if in a city after an earthquake. Hours of effort and our progress was barely a mile. We pitched our tiny tent and edged our exhausted bodies into the double layers of our one sleeping bag, stiff with hoar frost. Navigation was a problem, as the currents that swirl round the pole were sucking the pack ice towards the land, so our difficulties included a situation similar to going up the coming down side of an escalator. One night I felt our entire world shake and a rush like an express train passed under our heads. We realised that the ice floe that we were camping on was breaking up. A black line zig-zagged close to the guy-ropes. The sea! It was as if someone had dropped a jig-saw puzzle, with pieces of the tent, sledge and us scattered around. We loaded up our gear and pushed on ... no time for fear. I remember thinking that I did not mind if we all drowned, but how awful if the others did and I was left alone! Weeks passed. One morning I woke to feel that something was different ... I poked my head out of the tent and gazed at a miracle. The sun was above the horizon. Suddenly we were in a magic place, shafts of colour and sparkling crystals. I remembered the quotation 'a world without sun is like a life without love.' We were galvanised with energy, confident of our ability to reach the Pole.

Disaster struck a week later. Our radio went on fire. Without it, we would be unable to find the Pole or contact the party of scientists that we were to meet at that spot. The pack ice was melting ... if we were to get ourselves back to land we would have to hurry. Back we went; all the gruelling miles. We sighted land at last, but too late. A belt of open sea lay between it and us. I remember filling the primus with the last of our fuel and realising that without hot drinks we were doomed. The cold would beat us as we would be unable to keep up our body temperature as we breathed in the icy air. I paced the edge of the rotten ice, willing the floating blocks to drift together and so give us a chance. At three in the morning the wind rose ... the ice moved ... a bridge formed. I rushed for the others. We fixed on our skis and gingerly slid them forward, spreading out our weight as much as possible. The ice began to sway, to form a wave, but we must not hurry. A seal burst up, as astonished as we were to see him! Any pressure with our ski sticks broke the thin skin and a spurt of water froze in mid air. But we made it: We reached land, having attained farther north than any other unsupported party, to this day. Lessons that I learnt on that journey have stood me in good stead all the rest of my life. Self-reliance. To keep going on. To decide on priorities. To be glad to be alive! Everyone needs their own North Pole ... to have something to strive for. We thrive on stress and need to be stretched. The women of the 90s must have a goal and they have to look for it for themselves.

Transvestism in the Boardroom

ANNE SMITH

'Over the next ten years there won't be enough men to go around – so women will have to take on the really top jobs in our society' one of the editors of *Network*, the newsletter of an association of professional women, declares on the back page of the spring 1990 issue. On the front page, she explains what is behind that ominous, tremulous, 'have to':

> At an evening discussion earlier in the year, Network members looked at the barriers which were forming a 'glass ceiling'. We decided that one of the most powerful obstacles was our own inhibition in going for the most senior positions. Each of us at some time had felt a sneaking fear of success. This fear, combined with all the other forces ranged against us, had been enough to keep the glass ceiling intact. We even had difficulty imagining ourselves above the ceiling, which seems sometimes to be made of one-way glass.

After that discussion, a weekend convention was held. Among the women taking part were several senior managers 'just below board level, in public companies'. They addressed the question of the glass ceiling: being able to see the top, but not being able to get there. What they did not address – or not according to the conference report – was the 'powerful obstacle' of their own inhibitions. Nor did they seem to get any further as women than a mild recommendation to one another to assert their female virtues more in their business life.

> Until business and professional women come to terms with being women, there is not really a lot of hope for women as a whole. We will still be thought of and spoken of as one of those demanding, irritating minority groups to whom the occasional social-political sop must be thrown, although we actually form the majority of the population. We will still succeed in isolation, by starting our own businesses or creating something artistic, or getting the majority of the votes as a freak tie-breaker between two male candidates. But we will always as a group, be the playthings of fate: only when there are not 'enough men to go around' will women make it into the boardrooms; when there are too many men, it'll be back to the bedrooms.

Meanwhile the men at the top are already preparing for the shortage:

> Notionally, hierarchical structures within organisations are becoming flatter; there is a trend too towards smaller management teams, with responsibility being delegated further down the organisation than ever before. What this means is that just at the time when women's management potential is beginning to be seriously recognised, the opportunities to progress are becoming more and more limited.

Is this mere coincidence, or is it cause and effect?

What suggests that it might be cause and effect is the attitude shown by the women at the convention:

> One point that came out very strongly was the importance of breaking into male networks. We all admitted disliking the enforced drink in the pub or the game of golf. This is an essential part of building bridges with

colleagues – it makes us all seem part of the human race.

So the human race is male? And women, therefore, are inferior. The next logical step after the golf and the booze must be transvestism. It's already on the way, with 'power-dressing', female body-building, and the rise and rise of unisex (= male).

One inhibition is against claiming any sort of female superiority. How carefully this next point is made:

> However, I was pleased that everyone confirmed that they would not copy the rather out-dated 'male' methods of management. We felt that women had stronger values which we would not compromise. Lee stressed that research had shown that a degree of individuality made you stand out. What better outstanding quality than integrity?

It seems that the male method of management lacks integrity but we all knew that, and how a woman is to manage with integrity when all the men around her have happily surrendered theirs long ago is a question only the very naïve would attempt to answer. It's that 'Lee stressed that research had shown that a degree of individuality made you stand out' which really chills the blood.

As if you could choose how to be individual: 'Will I wear a pink shirt today, or will I behave with integrity?' These women seem to regard themselves as Dr Frankenstein and the monster rolled into one. In decrying the 'out-datedness' of male management, they confirm it. The self-made woman is just the self-made man a hundred and fifty years on. The female eunuch is alive and well and wearing shoulder-pads.

Where will professional women be in the year 2000? The Network convention came up with four pointers to success. The first is depressingly in line with all that has gone before:

We need to be twice as good as our male counterparts (we all know this already) and to be less humble about our achievements. Telling others about them enables us to become associated with success and to be seen as winners.

In the year 2000, professional women will be supermen; superior males.

The second takes up where the boasting leaves off:

We need to tell people what our career aspirations are – particularly the most senior managers. Otherwise, such assumptions as 'she has done well for a woman' and therefore (understood) 'she doesn't want to progress any further' came into play. In the year 2000, professional women will be openly on the make.

The third is rather more humble:

We need to aim to work in a section or department where our worth is actively recognised by the most senior people/person. A 'champion' is likely to provide development opportunities and, perhaps, open career doors.

In the year 2000, professional women will still depend on male help and approval.

The fourth contains a grain of hope which is programmed to self-destruct:

We need to make the most of the sort of skills and abilities we have as women (for example caring, insight, intuition, a willingness to learn from mistakes, etc.). Fortunately there is a growing recognition about the value of such attributes and even men are being encouraged to cultivate them instead of some of the more traditional macho qualities.

In the year 2000, you won't be able to tell a professional woman from a professional man. Who is encouraging the men to cultivate their caring, insight and intuition? Presumably other men: their bosses. 'Fortunately' ... 'even men' ... What comes through in all this report is women's frustration; they have compromised themselves into a corner from which they cannot escape without becoming men or waiting for the men to become women.

The picture this conjures up of the men who sit round the boardroom table is utterly disheartening; the glass ceiling is reinforced with invisible steel rods and at the end of the day women will not make it to the top just because they are women. The only safe way is to start your own business, but then it won't be easy to make those vital contacts in the pub or on the golf-course: you are practically limited to running a business, the end product of which will be consumed by women. *Body Shop*, *Laura Ashley* – their success is no coincidence either.

A version of this operates in the arts. When the Scottish Arts Council appointed a woman to be its overall Director, the first comments were comments of surprise or astonishment about the fact that she is a woman. Her background, the structure of the career that led to her appointment, were secondary considerations. It was like the second coming of Mrs Thatcher, complete with discreetly silent, faintly embarrassed men. So now we fear that this might be a downgrading of the Scottish Arts Council's status. Yet it is women who underpin the structure of arts organisations everywhere.

In this situation, it would be naïve to prophesy any great revolutionary change in the position of women in the year 2000. But then, it would be downright stupid to expect to correct in fifty years a situation that has prevailed for more than 2000. Much easier to prescribe than to prophesy. Except our prescriptions are all wrong too. Wendy Shillaim reported in *Network*:

> A major report out last month said that women who aim
> for the top can come up against unfair barriers – barriers
> which are so entrenched that it will take a major gov-
> ernment and social initiative to remove them. The
> Commission on Women at the Top, headed by Lady
> Howe and backed by the Hansard Committee, reported
> that women are blocked by outdated attitudes and work
> practices which, though not in themselves sexist, are
> leading to discrimination.

How on earth do you create change on this scale, at the
request of a commission headed by someone chosen for being
the wife of a famous man? Can anyone see the editor of the *Sun*
gathering his staff around him and saying, 'It's the end of the
road, boys – Lady Howe has said it's all got to change and we
start by dropping Page 3'?

There is change, but it is infinitesimal and largely confined
to the middle class. In order to predict where women will be in
the year 2000, you would have to know what the economic
situation in Britain will be, for it all comes back to that, and
not to anything of any significance that women will achieve for
themselves. Those outdated attitudes are as much ours as
theirs.

The Truth Thank You

FRANCES TAYLOR

It had been raining all afternoon. I ran across the road, not bothering to avoid the puddles, to the shop-side pavement. The nearest shelter was a cafe, I needed a break.

I enjoyed noticing the change in environment, standing for a few seconds I looked about, the door was open so the sounds of the street mingled with inside. The cappuccino machine hissed and gurgled amongst thick smokey voices. Someone was stacking cigars in the cut-off bottoms of plastic sweet jars which were being used like drawers for displaying rows of tobacco products.

I took off my sodden coat.

Then I noticed someone looking at me smiling. He was sitting with his back to the back wall on the aisle seat, an open briefcase on the table. His look made me feel as if I was meant to be meeting him and was just a wee bit late, his smile was almost reassuring me that I had been forgiven for my tardiness. He looked interested in what I was doing, possibly where I was going to sit too. He wore one of those suits which doesn't just have a single colour. The wool had been spun with many strands of colour and the fabric woven similarly in a subtle stripe, blues with distinct greens and mustards. I thought his eyes revealed that he could do with some sort of holiday, he'd obviously been thinking long and hard for the whole of eternity. The hand-me-down, battered and cracked leather case contained unthinkable chaos. The lid though was tidy, the right things were in the right pockets, I thought. He was still smiling, his eyes matched the suit.

I remembered a rainy day in the countryside of my child-hood. How, when the rain had stopped, I had stood dripping, witnessing the colours and textures with glee, I was in the ploughed field at the edge, where it was not quite ploughed and not quite meadow…I saw the small blue puddles amongst the stones, bare peaty earth and blades of wet grass. I saw how the beads of water wobbled the outlines in the wind. His suit creased and stretched each time he moved even slightly. There was already a coat on the radiator so I put mine over the pea-green scales in front of it. He was still smiling.

I smiled back. I made the decision to move past the other tables towards him. There was a definite yes to my joining him at his table. We laughed. Drips of rain rolled down his thick brown hair, there was the odd white one here and there and some was stuck onto his temples and cheeks. T.A. was the monogram on the case he'd closed and moved to make room, he asked if I wanted tea but I had noticed Horlicks on the sign above where my coat was dripping. He ordered two from the waiting waitress. He stretched out his hand and introduced himself to me as Timothy Antrobus. I leaned over a little and took his hand, 'Clare McGeever'. We laughed.

He questioned me, 'were you born on the seventeenth of October 1965 by any chance?' I hesitated, amazed and ex-cited… He persisted. 'Well?'

I had been born exactly twenty five years ago last Wednesday very early in the morning. I sat down. I nodded. Then I noticed my expression in the mirror. He looked aston-ished too but lost no time in asking me if I wanted to take part in his questionnaire devised for the post-graduate studies he was trying to complete. Two mugs, which I thought were a little small, clunked onto the table with saucers and spoons.

I spooned off the top froth, slurping slightly, he chose slurping noisily and got a silly moustache. It was delicious. The narrowness of the table made our conversation silly too. If we had both sat up with our elbows on it our noses would have undoubtedly touched but instead we were taking turns in adopting that forward enthusiastic posture, to an outsider it probably looked like some sort of avian courtship ritual. The rain was still pounding. Inside it was warm and sticky.

He was talking. He wanted to study my, his subject's, feelings towards the world from childhood to my perception of the truth now and how or if they were related. I studied him. Sure, I could do it. His laughter showed his appreciation.

I spied the time on the incongruous clock. I could have done it then but we agreed on the next evening at seven in this same outlandishly informal place. There was fun and spontaneity in his choice of setting. I stood and squeezed awkwardly out of the old ochre cinema seats and retrieved my coat. The rain had stopped so I draped it over my arm. We exchanged goodbyes and I walked out into the purple-grey of the late October storm clouds, home.

Seven rushed up at me. I had to run a bit to avoid being late. T.A. was in the same seat and there were two inviting mugs of Horlicks beside the familiar case. I was trembling. I thought of school, exams and tests. Was I any good? Would Daddy be proud of me? My bruised intelligence was hammering my head, on came feelings of mistrust of the world, those shitty bits I didn't feel able to explain or understand. I was feeling like I had just volunteered to take my clothes off in front of someone who may or may not abuse the situation. I didn't want to lie and cover up my feelings, one of them being that I bloody well would if I had to. I didn't want to act defensive. He was smiling, saying hello, pushing my mug nearer to me. I wondered what he was thinking while I squeezed back into my old seat. The Horlicks was just the right temperature to gulp down quickly but I sipped gently as he explained his ideas. He wanted to know what I felt when I was young and now... He continued speaking...

Clear bright images of my life and dreams streamed through my thoughts... school... school... school... school... sweat broke out on the base of my spine, my palms and armpits as the memories returned. I had felt small, smaller, smallest. Images of my pleading eyes my desperate face. I remembered the days before I went to the academy... running around sniffing things, yelling, screaming, playing, inventing. I cried then for the lost me. I remembered a pace of life that was completely mine. EVERYTHING was mine then to look at, to touch, to taste and to explore in any way that things invited. I found ways to get the world to reveal its secrets.

I know things from those hours of scientific, creative discovery. The tears burned my face a little. Then the academy came, with it hours of unadulterated boredom. Some of my teachers tried hard but not in the right way, not with enough thought and questioning. My mind, they were right, was beyond the walls of the uninspiring classroom, in my world, my real world, alive spontaneous and thinking. Some information came out of my teachers but now I question its usefulness, not the adding, subtracting, the structure of my language and the scientific truths known then, but the impatient nagging voices, scolding remarks, the constant threat of punishment and the plague of competition. A pecking order of an artificial struggle to be the best with the odds stacked on being the worst. My pace was drummed out of me, it didn't suit their rigid, frigid structure, it would have been too hard to control. It would need too much thought, time, energy and of course money, the great limiting factor. I had been ranked, processed, channelled through examinations against my peers and spat out at sixteen smothered in labels and grades. I knew what I wanted but there was no room for it there. There wasn't even a let-up in the creative classes, grades were handed out, smiles for the A's, the lucky F's got ignored, the unlucky ones got lumped with frowns and scowls or worse. I knew we were all equal, that this treatment was wrong but I didn't know how to fight them. These were adults, surely they knew things, I wanted to love and be loved, I desperately wanted to trust them.

Why then did life feel so bad, what should I have done with all that boredom, the state of sedation I had felt in the classroom. I used to try and talk with my classmates, a big mistake, or I'd scribble surreptitious notes, apparently bad and disrespectful. No-one considered what I felt about how my time was spent. Detention.

My heart screamed about the boredom and lies it knew were wrong but the adults were so big, so many, so uncompromising, stifled by history and tradition. I had wanted to cry and shout but that was bad, naughty, nothing to do with me recovering from the damaging onslaught of history and tradition. If only they had just listened... listened... listened...

He sat listening, ignoring his own want for tears perpetuating the lie about tears and him. I felt the long ago rumbles of having to give up my dreams or at least push them well out of sight to accommodate the ancient idea of education and do what was good for me.

I gazed out the cafe door's window through the mirror. It was dark outside but for the sodium lamps and car headlights.

I felt numb. I wished for something to happen, he urged me on…what about the truth…what the hell is it…I felt like I'd never known…but I did know… I hadn't lost it. Maybe, it could never be lost. It was smouldering inside, all that hard learning operating on the outside. Perhaps it is the batterings that I, as a child, endured unchecked that is obscuring it from view…that means all I must do is peep through the blanket, peel the shell, I shuddered it was so simple!

He was watching me closely. The Horlicks was cooler but still good, I finished it tipping my head back and letting the last drips run into my mouth. I almost clunked the saucer with the mug but stopped just before and placed it carefully. So what was my truth…what would I change… My head was whirling, ideas were shooting about, I let them. I felt teeming excitement over tiny but great possibilities. Freedom from the pain of my past, constant emergence, communication of the truth and real rational thinking. For sure I have never needed oppression or lies the poison of growth and progression. I want to giggle with mistakes, juggle with information and wallow in love. I was aware of the strait-jacket deposited by my past…squirming beneath lay a host of lithe potential. I imagined a real world of beauty, bright humans scraped clean, glowing everywhere… I revelled… I could see the truth. I think he could too.

Armageddon

VALERIE THORNTON

Armageddon sleeps in the church and lives in the park where he is walking to Sullom Voe.

The church where he sleeps is long since abandoned by all but the god on the wall. This is a Jesus, in blue and gold mosaic, high above Armageddon's head. His open arms are inviting Armageddon to be blessed. 'Come unto me' is cut into the red sandstone to his right, with 'Blessed are the poor' on his left.

When the wind whips through the ragged lace of the stained glass windows, Armageddon curls below the hood of his mousy duffle-coat, sheltering beneath the shattered ribs of the upturned organ. He knows if he uncurls and stares for long enough at the pale pointed oval on the end wall of the transept, his Jesus will materialise in the gloom and bless him, because he is poor.

Armageddon makes fairly regular sacrificial offerings to his god of polo mints, dog food and El Dorado. The polo mints are a luxury. It is enough that the god, who cannot eat, can see them. Armageddon eats them for him.

Armageddon knows the whore of Babylon lives behind lace curtains in a tenement flat opposite his church and that if he doesn't melt into his church, shadowy as the night, then the bitch will call the police.

They pick their way over the rotten floorboards, their

torches staggering over the peeling walls until they pick him out and put him on the street. They're OK though. After the whore of Babylon lets fall her evening velvet curtains with a heavy rustle of self-righteousness, Armageddon walks around the block and back home again.

Armageddon belongs to the church as much as the church belongs to him. He will tell you this as you walk through his park.

He is a slight figure, pale, with fine skin drawn over his features which are sharpened by many hungers. His chin sticks out like the man in the moon, with a tiny mouth above it. Only the slightest of dark hairs above the corners of his thin lips suggest he's male. He has lost all his teeth, and his voice, light as a bird, gives nothing away.

'Bless you, Joseph!' he says, falling into step with you, however many you are, and whatever sex.

'Bless you, Joseph!' he says again, struggling to extract a new map of Scotland from the pocket of his duffle coat. 'I'm walking to Sullom Voe. It's just over there,' he says, pointing in a northerly direction, towards the far side of the park. 'You been there, Joseph?'

'No, it's a bit far for me. Why are you going there?'

'I am about my father's business,' he announces, folding the map all against the preset creases and stuffing it into his pocket.

His eyes are a little sticky and there are cobwebs on the hood of his duffle coat, but his fine black hair is clean and soft.

'My name is Armageddon. I have bone in my head which doesn't belong to me. Look!'

And from his pocket he takes a grubby bird skull, small, like a thrush or blackbird. His slender pale fingers turn it this way and that, with careful knowledge of its delicacies.

'Look at it and it will be in your head too, and you will be blessed. When the circles of the years are complete, you will be on the inside too, with the rest of us. See over there, Joseph?' He points to the far side of the river, to a dark space below a mossy stone lintel, with water lapping at its lip. 'That's where I was shut behind the stone. With Mary, my mother.'

He swerves from your side to a bed of purple crocuses at the edge of the path and picks up a pebble.

'This is the same stone. It has become small with the passing of years. Soon, when the centuries turn around, it will be nothing. It is accursed from the beginning of time.'

Armageddon hurls the stone into the river.

'The trees have all been killed too,' he says.

'Yes, but they'll soon get their leaves again, in the summer, won't they?'

'Maybe, I don't know. I'm not of this time. I don't see things the way you do,' he waves his thin fingers up and down the river. 'I don't know the day or the month or the week or the decade or the season. They've taken my brain away. I'm old. Very, very old. In fact, I'm mummified. Yet underneath, I'm still wrapped in my swaddling clothes. This, my raiment, was once white.'

It's difficult to know what to say, so you say nothing.

'See that sandbank over there?' he continues.

It doesn't look like a sandbank. It's covered in last year's long grass, combed pale by the winter. It supports several leafless trees.

'When I was little my father was a carpenter. He made a basket of rushes and floated me on the river.'

'That must have been fun!'

He laughs and nods at the memory of it.

'He called me Armageddon.'

'Doesn't that meant the end of the world?'

'No, the world can't end. It says world without end.' Up ahead, leaning against the railings, staring at nothing in the river below, is an old man. His face is dark as autumn, his black clothes shabby and indistinguishable. As Armageddon draws level with him, he falls out of step and approaches the old man.

'How're you doing, Joe?' he says, offering him a polo mint.

Armageddon spends a long time, even in his timeless wilderness in the park, looking for Sullom Voe. By the time he gets back to his church, late in the evening, it has shrunk almost to nothing. There, instead of a roof to shelter below, instead of the narrow passage up to the broken way-in window, there is nothing but a big empty muddy space.

It is almost the end of the world for Armageddon, but for some reason, Jesus is still waiting for him. The transept wall, which adjoins the tenements next door, still stands, like a bookend, with a few feet of red sandstone walls on either side of Jesus, who is now opening his arms for the whole poor world to see. There is no roof, but the remainder of the wall, projecting on either side, provides some shelter. The whore of Babylon's curtains are drawn tight shut.

It is a night for Noah and by morning Armageddon is chilled to the bone. Above him, his Jesus looks over his head to the repair garage down the road, secure and smug with its white pebble-dash walls.

Armageddon, his clothes stiff with mud and many rains, is walking through the park talking to no-one in particular.

'I'm a fully qualified architect, you know, Joseph. Without papers. They've taken everything away. Car, bank cards, credit cards, stocks and shares. They've taken my brain too. Left me with nothing.'

He has a fine beard curling around his chin, and his duffle coat is stained and torn. Most of his map has long gone except for the Shetland Isles which he ate.

'I have a castle in my kingdom over there,' he says, pointing south, towards the distant towers of the hospital. 'But I have to be in the wilderness now. For forty days and forty nights until Sullom Voe comes to pass. That old man's in my castle; he had a heart attack. They wouldn't have taken him in if they'd known he was related to me. No-one'll take me in.'

Beside Armageddon prances a white charger, reduced to the form of a small mongrel which he is feeding with dirty polo mints.

'I am old enough to see now,' he continues, 'and I can see many homes in my head. Many little homes inside my church. For all the whores of Babylon who will be left behind when the years turn around.'

And while these things were coming to pass, Armageddon slept within the scaffolding, within the shells of flats which were rising from the ashes of his church. There was no more Jesus to come unto him, they had knocked him off the wall to make way for many bricks. But now it didn't matter. Jesus was in Armageddon's head, bright as remembrance, below the hood of his duffle coat.

When all the whores of Babylon were installed in their new quarters, when the years had turned around from the time when the poor were blessed, yet another casualty was found huddled cold as stone below his duffle coat in the park. His name was unknown, as was his age, and the message in the grey crumbs of bone and polo mint in his pocket was indecipherable.

Extracts from *Scotland The Brave – And Me*

JOAN URE

Joan Ure was a pioneer. She was almost alone among Scottish women writers of her generation in writing primarily for the stage - most public and in some ways most punishing of literary forms. In plays like *I See Myself as This Young Girl, Something In It for Cordelia, Take Back Your Old Rib Then,* and *The Lecturer and the Lady* she wrote with wit and the allusive concentration of a poet about women's divided lives and their place on the margins of many worlds. She was also one of the few to articulate, in her occasional writings, a sense of the beleaguered position of the woman writer in Scotland. Her too-early death in 1978 robbed the Scottish stage and Scottish women of one of their most original voices.

This extract, from an article which appeared in *Scottish International Review* in 1968, shows her quirky, tenacious individuality. It might also cause us to reflect on just what has changed during these 20 years.

I am a writer, a real writer, that is I can't be bought off when it comes to the Word. I like being a writer on the margin of my daily existence, in the way that people used to say their prayers at night, so that the next day might begin joyful. I know I am part of a minority. I do not need everybody to love me. One or two or three or four — this makes for me a nice little crowd. A party. With wine and little cakes.

Suddenly I wasn't at home here.

Perhaps I had grown a bit self-confident? I mean I felt confident that, if I had a thought and a need to express it, it wasn't a bad thing to do that. I admit even to going a step further. I decided that in this place where only bloodshed and argument are entered into with any spirit, I would let my whole self free without my arguments and without even a hatpin. I would adventure with my imagination. And not be much afraid. Because nothing could get at anything about me that mattered. I haven't got a great thing about virginity. It seemed to me more generous to give than to keep. It may be I thought it was love. But I don't know. I admit that. I haven't got an argument one way or another.

Then it was as if the place – Scotland – got up and threatened me. As if there was something about me that was getting on the nerves of the Zeitgeist. As if my heart were carefree and yet not careless enough. There is a brute force at the centre of the Zeitgeist and brute force needs you to carry at least a hatpin, or else it is left to feel ridiculous. It always takes Soldiers to guard the Zeitgeist. You are a nationless creature, a child of the inter-nations, just the equal of anyone anywhere, alone but not segregated, when you haven't got your Soldiers. When you haven't at least got your gang …

. . .

When Lord Reith appeared on television, I wanted to console that solemn man who took his life so seriously as if it were all he had. 'Don't mind feeling that sense of your personal failure. It means you really had a sort of mission' I wanted to tell him. And continued. 'And if once and for all you could do anything, you would be certain to know it was bad.' He was explaining how he had a vocation.

The hallucination came the next day. Perhaps because Lord Reith was such a big man.

It was a dark day and what happened was in the form of an expectation. I expected round every counter to meet John Knox. Yet even his statue used to scare me when I was yearly through in Edinburgh for the Festival. I'd be going up the Assembly stairs for a performance of theatre in the rectangular. John Knox stands on that pedestal on your left, counting heads, and segregating them, and he is very much taller than anyone passing. Normally it is impossible not to take him seriously and I know it's because of his height. Yet that dark day, if I had met him in Glasgow, grounded by the diesel and by the season's sales, I know I would have recognised him and I'd have immediately tried to convert him. Of course, I would have begun quite tactfully and yet without servility, and I would have mentioned how I respected some of his insights, especially those he learned before he was famous, while he was serving as a galley slave for speaking out of turn. There is nothing like being a slave for teaching you quickly and yet finally that men are naturally equal and entitled to express an opinion on any subject whatever. But what I wanted to put to him is that if he'd been less solemn, then his countrymen wouldn't have had the model that has led them on to selfrighteousness such as it would be difficult to find anywhere else in the world. "If you'd been a wee man," I'd have said "such solemnity would have been ridiculous, and we would have been saved so much."

I mean that I wanted to convert him to the idea of playfulness, as a nourishing idea. Maybe a duty.

Yet he wouldn't have listened. He had that little unworthy prejudice against women with opinions and a person's prejudices.

"Oh Jane Austen!" I was calling out from my bed in the darkness. It was, naturally, night. "Oh, Cassandra, they'd have called even your sister Jane's talent maidenly. Not little, because she wrote these long things. But maidenly they would have said here. And that would have meant her insights were bound to be unimportant, you see.

I spoke rather to Cassandra than to Jane, for although Jane Austen is officially dead, she is, I am sure, still working. So I told Cassandra the things I needed to tell to somebody just at that sad point in time. She was a good listener. She'd had practice. "They'd never notice here that with some pretty delicately balanced language you can make many an adventurous point," I said. "And the famous shock words of tomorrow may turn out to be 'discreet' and 'forgive'." I went on, because it is the way you do in the paranoid moments that, with any luck, everyone gets to go through to give their insights more energy. I said, "Some acceptable methods of shocking an audience, used again and again, Cassandra, are indistinguishable from plagiarism after a while." Of course I stopped for breath. But not for long. "What one is saying, if it takes some saying, may be neither fragile nor false and yet the language may be choosey," I said. "And oh Cassandra, please turn away if what I say next offends you because you are a kind woman and I wish you were here ... but let me say it this once and for ever after be silent ... I never, never doubt a man's virility because, since love is more complicated than vigour is, his approach may not be like rape. I mean, oh I mean, Cassandra, that I know *they* have talent. Why don't *they* know about *me*?"

I didn't talk for a while after that. Not to Cassandra or anybody. The next person I talked to was to Leonard. I liked him because of his beauty on television and because Virginia

Woolf had trusted herself to him. I told him, in confidence and as gently as I could possibly do it, that if Virginia had ever been invited to an Edinburgh literary salon – not that it was likely – they'd have set her to butter the bannocks while the Real Poets got on with the chat. I didn't have to tell Leonard that when people are hungry, you choose to be buttering bannocks but it is nice when it's a choice. I am, as Leonard was, for nourishment of every kind. But I couldn't tell the Leonard who had so delicately survived his not more delicate Virginia that he wouldn't have been allowed up here even to protect her for he would have died here of the cold.

What I am trying to say is that I hadn't the ear of the Zeitgeist. I felt a clenched fist in my face. And because I am a female, and still a female, I feared and I feared and I feared for my good, sensitive looks. I wanted my good, sensitive looks. I was going to miss them.

I did not go mad last winter. It is more that I had come sane. It was very uncomfortable. So I realise it was probably a genuine visitation. With all the resultant difficulties of communication for a while. But I am bound to rejoice about it, of course, in the manner of every convert. It was a murky night I was seeing – gey murky – but at least I was, as they say, privileged to be seeing it.

The sprig of heather my aunt knitted into a tea-cosy for me was no use to me now. It wasn't enough. For hope's sake and for heaven's sake, I was bound to take to drink. I had found, like Hugh MacDiarmid long before me, that it takes a drunk to look hard at the thistle. It can't be faced stonecold sober. Gentleness dies in pain.

I am trying to say that I don't like it here. Suddenly. Yet where can I go, for I'm scarred? I'd be recognisable although

I've hardly a trace of an accent and never wear the kilt. I am trying to say that what I am saying is loaded. That utterance is not all. Just the best one can do.

The Scarecrow

RUTH WALKER

The young girl pushes open the farmhouse door. She is fresh faced, enthusiastic. The kitchen smells warm and inviting – a mixture of soapy washing, warm milk, bread and fruit. Life is like a dream for the girl at the minute, she arranges the wild flowers she has picked in a vase. Outside, the pine woods give a sweet aroma. A dusty track leads away down to the fields. She can hear the workmen chatting and laughing. By the back door a cat shifts in the sun, and the girl sits down beside it, raising her face to catch every drop of warmth, before she has to go in to prepare the meal.

Round and round I polish my zinc plate, preparing it for etching. It is the delicious moment of indecision. My face stares back at me from the shiny surface. I wonder, as I rub, what image I will draw on the clean surface. I keep coming back to something which preoccupies me at the moment - scarecrows - big, flapping creatures, sardonic in their stillness, reminders of the brevity of existence, with their battered bodies and cast off clothes, arms held out, cruciform. I make arabesques with the soft, dark wax, and begin to draw my idea.

The young girl goes out from the kitchen with her knife and basket. Usually one of the men brings in the vegetables for the soup, but to-day they must have forgotten. She crosses the yard and goes through the wicket gate. Flowers and vegetables grow in profusion alongside one another. She deftly cuts cabbages from the dusty soil, pulls carrots, turnips. A shiny black tarpaulin flaps gently on top of a hay rick. The vivid daisies and marigolds wink back at her. She stretches her back and gazes over, past the scarecrow, to the shed. She looks, and looks again, then turns away hastily. She sees two people at the window – two heads – she knows one of them and frowns slightly, and picks up her basket, and slowly turns away to go back to the house. A big cloud seems to cover the sun for a few moments. The air, which had been so fresh and sweet a moment ago, is suddenly dank and gloomy. Her load seems suddenly heavy.

As I draw, my idea takes shape. The scarecrow, its big white head turned sideways, stands among the cabbages. Behind are the pine trees, the clouds in the sky. I draw savagely, pressing deeper. You can just see the shed behind the scarecrow. I draw two heads at the window. I make them small. They are not interested in the drama of nature outside – clouds scudding past, rooks in the tall trees, cabbages rotting away in the ground. What was the head of the scarecrow made of? Was it, perhaps, an old enamel basin, corroded at the edges, bashed and worn? I remember it was white, and the scarecrow wore black, dusty old clothes. The scarecrow is the real hero of the piece – all seeing, inscrutable, silently suffering and decaying.

The girl goes back to the house. She feels there are eyes everywhere – the dark, unblinking windows, guarding their secrets. Even the trees stare out at her, unsmiling. She goes about her tasks woodenly, mechanically. She had been a stranger here herself three years ago, and now she knows all the ropes, who likes what for their lunch, she cuts the vegetables very finely – her husband gets annoyed if she cuts them coarsely. Strange. He is so unfussy in other ways – leave all this, he sometimes would say – let's go out to the woods today, and take a picnic – the sun is shining – life is young – don't keep your apron tied so tightly – the girl looks down at her shape now – she is plumper than when she arrived, a skinny waif.

The house, the farm and the gardens which seemed so big to her once, now feel like home. These are her buildings, cooking pots, and pine trees. She smooths her hands over her skirt, at least her child will belong to her, she frowns as she remembers the events of the morning. Her husband appears at the door, suddenly – he is always giving her little frights like that.

'Hey, why so sad? Come on, love. Don't you see the sun is shining? And how is that soup coming on? Smells good,' and he walks off smiling.

The girl stands still. Her limbs feel heavy, dead. She jumps as her mother-in-law comes in to the kitchen.

'Mercy, what's wrong, child. You're so still – are you alright?'

'Oh, yes, mother. I just – well, I just had a fright!'

'Did Peter make you start? He was always the same – even when he was a little boy.'

But the girl is not listening – she is far away – she is thinking about what she has just seen in the shed window. Secretly, she knows her happiness is too good to last, and Peter, she does not really know him so well, although she is married to him. He is so much older than her – she is in a strange country. Men think of women differently out here. He calls her his little chick, his tiny bird. He expects her to be soft and delicate, like a flower, but he insists on his good midday meal and she must wash and scrub. She never really minded till now. She enjoys being his willing slave, but will it always be so? What if he grows tired of her? or if she is ill – perhaps Peter has already grown tired of her – she must not brood any longer. She sees the workmen coming through the trees back for their lunch. To-day, she wonders what they think of her – usually they are so deferential to her. She almost imagines they are speaking about her as they pass the window – she can't understand their dialect.

I place the etching plate carefully in the acid bath, and stand at a respectful distance, watching as the lines on the plate hiss and bubble. I watch the head of the scarecrow slowly being consumed by the tiny bubbling lines I have drawn. I can hardly see the couple at the shed window, they are so blurred with bubbles. I stroke the lines with a feather, feeling the lines growing deeper.

The girl is sitting in the garden with her mother-in-law. The baby is lying crowing in his pram. Her husband comes past, and stops. He tickles the child.

'Ah, you are perfect – you are my beauty, my all – all this' – he waves his arms at the child – 'all this land – these woods – one day they will be yours!'

The girl stares sullenly ahead. She was right – Peter is not really interested in her. Her mother-in-law shifts in her chair.

'Peter, why must you be out in these woods so long – you used to stop and have some tea with us – don't drive yourself so hard.'

'But I must, mother, I must keep on.'

The girl says nothing. Silently, she wonders what she owns – her child – but he will grow up and speak the language better than she can. He belongs here. She watches a cloud scudding past in the sky. Quite suddenly she says that she wants to go home.

I press the black, oily ink into the lines on my etching plate, and then smooth the surplus off gently, coaxing the surface clean again. I wipe the scarecrow's head particularly clean, so that it will stand out, skull like. The bubbles from the acid have corroded into its whiteness, like a worm penetrating an apple. I stand back and admire the first print. It is a shock to see the image in reverse. The plate needs reworking, to give it added depth and richness. I decide to decorate the scarecrow with badges, like a battered war hero.

The girl sees things more clearly when she comes home. The baby is still with her mother-in-law. It is strange how much the girl enjoys doing simple things again on her own, like catching a bus into town, or deciding what she shall have for lunch. She misses the farm house, and the feeling of security she had with Peter. She goes back once or twice, to see how her child is getting on. Anna, the big strong girl from the farm, who used to work in the kitchen, is looking after her son. Peter is more obsessed than ever with planting more and more trees, and is always outside at work. The girl watches the family.

It is when they are all sitting down at the big diningroom table at the front of the house that the truth dawns upon her. Her mother-in-law sits vaguely uneasy. Peter is at the head of the table as usual. The girl thinks how like a wizened apple he has become, with all this fresh air. Anna comes downstairs, having put the child to bed. The girl sees her husband's face light up when Anna comes into the room. Then, as Anna serves the soup, she sees her husband just touch the big farm girl's arm. The girl notices the flash of electricity in Anna's face. Outside the window, some workmen pass who have been working late in the fields. She remembers enough of the

language to understand their sniggers, and coarse remarks.
Away in the distance a bull bellows. Anna begins to clear
away the dishes noisily. The mother-in-law sighs.

'She is a good girl, that Anna, only so ...'

'She is one of the best, the very best – she has such strong
arms and she loves my little son,' Peter tells his wife.

The girl thinks of the scarecrow in the garden. Each time
she returns, it looks more dilapidated and sad. She remembers
the heads in the window – so long ago now – was the other
head Anna? She can't be sure.

It feels warm and safe working in the printmaking studio.
The air is thick with the warm, oily smell of printing ink, and
crisp paper. I clean up the black ink on my slab with a big
palette knife, creating new patterns on the smooth stone. I
always like it when everyone else has gone home, and I am left
to tidy up slowly, on my own. I am pleased with the edition of
my new 'Scarecrow' print. Perhaps I will include it in my
exhibition – my mind races on, full of good ideas. It is strange
how life has turned out. I left Peter a long time ago now, and
I have never really looked back. The quiet discipline of the
studio suits me. I like the students who come here – how
young they all look.

But they have all gone home for Christmas. I don't really
like the thought of Christmas and New Year spent on my
own, so I make the tidying up last for a long time. I have the
radio on for company, and I half listen to its crackling chatter.
I clean off the ink from my hands, and begin to gather my
things. I am standing over the wash basin, and I look startled
at my reflection in the cracked mirror above. My hair shows
wispy white bits. A long, hot bath would be nice. There is
music on the radio now – Christmassy, and nostalgic. The

shops will be crowded on the way home. I go into the office, and unpack the bottle that the last of the students presented to me before he left.

'See you in the New Year, 1990, and all that!'

I remember the pine trees, and the big house in the country. The radio plays on. I see my face in the mirror, swimming before me. I raise my glass to my reflection, and, with a pang, remember my child.

The Last Camp

Lys Wyness

She was aware of the little boy, standing a few yards in front of her. He stood silent and still, waiting. She looked at his shoes, the colour of her dress. She did not want to look into the boy's face but did not know why. If she could remember why, the memories would come back. The boy took a step forward and still she did not look at his face. Grey shoes, his first shoes had been grey.

The woman sitting next to her on the bench was knitting. She would ask her presently if she would give her some wool. She could knit; bright jumpers, little boy colours. She longed to get fingers, her hands around the wool, the needles. The calming concentration, plain purl rows, one after the other. Just think about the knitting. She would ask the woman for blue wool. The boy was at her knee now, looking at her, wordless. 'Who is he?' she asked the woman, 'Who is this boy?' The woman answered, but did not halt her knitting. 'He will be gone on Friday, they take them away on Fridays.' The boy put a hand on her knee and she looked down on the little fat fingers, spread out, claiming her knee. She saw the tiny dimple on each knuckle and she stroked the fingers, one by one, then looked into his face. A round baby face, soft peaches, moist red lips. His eyes were set deep and she bent a little and looked into them and saw the pale blue eyes watching her. She drew him gently towards her and clasped him with her knees. 'Who are you boy?' She curved her hand over his head and felt the familiar fine silky hair, she rubbed a strand through her fingers and he clambered onto her lap. Instinctively she rocked the boy and he laid his head on her breast, sighed and slept. She breathed deep, through her nostrils, smelling him, the sweetness of his body, and she remembered something.

'Can I have some wool?' she whispered to the woman, but the woman turned away and did not answer. Blending in with the buildings. The people wore grey, melding with the stone. Grey clothes, faces, hair, invisible against the buildings, no identity. The boy was sleeping, his breathing even. A fine mist was on his forehead and his hair was damp. His bottom lip hung loose and dribbled a clear dewdrop, she caught it with her finger and sucked it and remembered something.

She would ask the woman again. 'Who is this boy? Is this my boy?' The woman halted in her knitting and stared into the middle distance. 'This is the last camp,' she said. 'He will be taken away on Friday.' She resumed her knitting. The boy slept on. His head was heavy on her breast and she shifted slightly, he trembled a little at the movement and opened his eyes for a moment but did not see, he was still asleep. His head had left a damp patch on her grey dress, she smoothed it and passed her moist hand over her face, smelling the child's hot sweet sweat. She remembered some more.

A hole, the biggest hole. They had built the city from that hole. A grey city. A city with sharp edges. Tall grey buildings, grey streets. She did not want to be grey. Blue, pink, lilac, green, yellow, she wore colours. Grey was a hole, not a colour. She sang softly to the boy and the woman knitted. Presently she asked the woman, 'Have I been here long?'

'You came with me, remember? We've been through all the camps. We're clear now, all clear. This is the last one.'

'The last one,' she said softly to the boy and pushed his damp hair behind his ears, 'It's the last one.'

'Not for him' the woman whispered, 'He goes on Friday.'

'Where?'

'They take them, the healthy ones. A quota here, a quota there. Could be anywhere. A good life, he'll be fine. He'll forget all this.'

'All what?'

'You know!'

But she didn't know, she didn't know, she could only remember the dreams. He was just a little boy, two, three years maybe? She held him closer to her body. 'He's not a quota' she said to the woman, 'this little boy, he's not a quota.' The woman held out her knitting and pulled it this way and that. 'The Americans take them, or the Frenchies; they'll forget.' The boy gave a shuddering sigh and grasped at her arm and went limp again. She looked at his blue veined eyelids and fair lashes. One eyelid was not completely closed and he watched her unseeing from the slit. She remembered.

A Government order. They filled in the hole. Politicians came, scientists came, troops came. It would never leak, they said. It was safe, they said. The owners of the hole took the money and left the city. 'Did they go to America?' she asked. 'America, Canada, Europe, they all take their quota' the woman said. 'They bring them up as their own. He'll be a Yank.' She spat on the dusty ground and cast off some stitches.

She knew where she was now. They had brought her here with the others in the lorries. But she had been here before, long ago, before the sickness. She remembered it, a valley

surrounded by hills. Thermals, up-surges from the hills. The
gliders would shush in the air like tin birds. They would lie
and watch. Lie on the springy heather and count; seven, eight,
nine, floating, stiff winged birds under puffy clouds. That was
long ago but this was the place. She knew it, she remembered.
The boy opened his eyes and blinked, he put a hand upon her
breast and stroked it dreamily, they both remembered.

The boy was sucking his thumb and watching the woman
knitting. 'I know this place,' she whispered in his ear; he
wriggled. 'Not far from here I saw them, all those years ago,
aside a burn. This is the time of year. The encampment. They
will be there still.' The boy listened intently.

'The boo-backed tents, the camp fires with the dark women
smoking pipes. The men with their horses and wagons. And
bairns, like you, and dogs tumbling over and over on the
grassy slopes. I know them. An easy mind, that's what they'll
give you boy, an easy mind.'

She took his hand and they walked from the last camp.
Walked away from the woman knitting, she was counting her
stitches and did not look up. Walked past the moor and when
the boy grew tired she carried him along the road lined with
silver birches and coconut scented golden whin. Along the
path through the wood till they reached the encampment by
the burn.

Notes on Contributors

ROWENA ARSHAD was born in Brunei, grew up in Penang, moved to England in 1977 and on to Edinburgh in 1985. She has worked with Scottish Education and Action for Development and in the Multicultural Education Centre. In January 1991 she will take up a lectureship at Moray House College of Education. She was a co-founder of the Scottish Black Women's Group, founder of the Women Worldwide Group to highlight issues of concern to all women, and is a member of Lothian Black Forum, where men and women campaign together on black issues. This dual commitment is also clear in her contributions to several publications on the position of black women in Scotland. Among her many other interests are the history and culture of the Highlands.

ELIZABETH BURNS lives in Edinburgh. Her poetry has appeared in various magazines and anthologies, including *Original Prints* 2 & 3. *a united Europe?* was one of the six prizewinning entries in the competition.

ALISON CAMERON was born in Ayrshire and now lives in Glasgow. Teaching English in an Ayrshire secondary school and studying for an M. Ed at Glasgow University provided the raw material for this article. She has subsequently been seconded to Strathclyde Region's Equal Opportunities Team. Her article was one of the six prizewinning entries in the competition.

KAY CARMICHAEL grew up in the East End of Glasgow. She trained as a psychiatric social worker and is now a writer, broadcaster and a freelance consultant with a particular interest in ways of making social services accountable to the people who use them. As a socialist she constantly seeks to link the personal and the political and her most enduring commitment is to those who fail to meet society's norms of conformity.

ANN COLTART is a freelance journalist working in Glasgow and the west of Scotland. Before moving north, she was an adult literacy lecturer in London. She initiated women's writing groups there and found them crisper on deadlines than any editor. Her work was commended in the competition.

JANET DAVIDSON lives, works, paints and walks in Strathspey where she tries to make peace and space for writing. She would like to change the world but is still trying to work out how to do it. Her work was commended in the competition.

ROSIE FURLONG was born in Easter Ross and is a graduate of the Glasgow School of Art, now living and teaching in Ayrshire. Though she has done some illustrative work for *Yachting Monthly*, this is the first written piece to be published. *Name A Dozen Women Artists* was one of the prizewinning entries in the competition.

PAT GERBER was born in Glasgow in 1934. She is a freelance writer, reviewer of children's books for the *Glasgow Herald*, radio, and Scottish Television, and she runs classes in Writing for Pleasure at Glasgow University. Her fiction has been published in anthologies such as *New Writing Scotland*, in *Scottish Field*, and broadcast on BBC radio. She is currently working on a book for children. Her work was commended in the competition.

MAGI GIBSON was born in 1953, lives near Stirling with her family. Poems previously published in two Women's Anthologies – *Recurring Themes* and *Fresh Oceans* – as well as the *Scotsman* and *Radical Scotland*. *The Senile Dimension* was one of the six prizewinning entries in the competition.

KATHLEEN JAMIE was born in Renfrewshire in 1962 and grew up in Midlothian. She studied Philosophy at Edinburgh University. Her first book of poetry, *Black Spiders* (published by Salamander Press, 1982) won a Gregory award and a Scottish Arts Council Book Award.

HELEN LAMB is a graduate of Glasgow University and now lives in Dunblane with her three children. Her work has previously appeared in *Original Prints 2*, *Fresh Oceans*, *Scottish Child* and been broadcast on Radio 4's Morning story. Her entry won a prize in the competition.

LIZ LOCHHEAD, poet and playwright, was born in Motherwell and studied at Glasgow School of Art. Over the years her work has become more public, moving from the engagingly individual persona of her first book of poems, *Memo for Spring*, to a preoccupation with legend and history, and with the multiple roles involved in drama, translation, and performance art. Much of this has concerned women, some Scottishness, and some very strikingly both *(Mary Queen of Scots Got Her Head Chopped Off)*.

RONNIE MCDONALD is a trade union official at the Scottish Trades Union Congress. A considerable part of her work is devoted to issues which affect women, not only in trade unions, but in society generally. She produces a quarterly magazine for women trade unionists in Scotland and is a member of the Scottish Low Pay Unit Advisory Group. She is a director of 7:84 Scottish Peoples' Theatre.

ANNE MACLEOD was born in the Highlands, of Anglo-Irish parents. She studied medicine at the University of Aberdeen, but has lived and worked in Inverness ever since. Writing is a recently acquired obsession, but she has had work published in various places, notably *Lines Review* and *Understanding*.

ALISON MILLAR was born in Bradford, Yorkshire, in 1964, and now lives in Alloa. She is currently working as a journalist with a local radio station. She is actively involved with Alloa Writers' Circle, and performs her work locally. *Walking Back* was a prizewinning entry in the competition.

WILMA MURRAY was born in 1939 in Aberdeenshire. Studied Geography at Aberdeen University. After teaching for a number of years, she started writing seriously in 1983, with stories published mainly in Scottish magazines and various anthologies, including *Original Prints 1* and *2* and most recently *Three's Company*, Keith Murray Publications.

TESSA RANSFORD lives in Edinburgh, as she has done most of her life, although she was born in India and spent some years again as an adult in Pakistan. She has written poetry in the context of a busy, practical life. Director of the Scottish Poetry Library and editor of *Lines Review*. Since the mid-Seventies, she has had six books published, of which the most recent are *Shadows from the Greater Hill*, a poem sequence based on the view of Arthur's Seat from her flat, and *A Dancing Innocence*, a selection published in 1988. Her poem was commended in the competition.

MYRTLE SIMPSON is a renowned explorer and skier, writer of many travel, biographical and children's books, and a member of the Scottish Sports Council. The first woman to ski across Greenland, she also reached the most northerly point ever by a woman on an 'unsupported' expedition. She thinks that some present day trends offer great opportunities to women if they would take them.

ANNE SMITH, a Fife miner's daughter, is a woman of letters as well as a doctor of philosophy; literary critic, radio playwright, novelist, editor, journalist and reviewer, founder of *The Literary Review* and chief executive of Book Trust Scotland. She has collected and published women's reminiscences of their past – as personal and emotional histories rather than social history archive material – and in her novel *The Magic Glass* explores the situation of being born female into the Scottish working class.

VALERIE THORNTON was born in 1954, in Glasgow. Gave up teaching English five years ago, and has had a variety of odd jobs including work on feature films, film festivals, picture research and writing advertising copy. Currently subtitling for the BBC and teaching creative writing. Has published poems and short stories in various literary magazines and anthologies including *Lines Review, Cencrastus, New Writing Scotland, Streets of Gold* and *Scottish Short Stories*. Now working on a screenplay. Her work was commended in the competition.

RUTH WALKER was born in Brechin, Angus, and grew up there and at Kemback, Fife. She trained as a painter at Edinburgh College of Art in the sixties, and she has designed and made stained glass windows, and taught printmaking in the south, as well as exhibiting paintings. She gave up full time teaching in 1984. Her stories have appeared in *Accents of Fife*, the magazine of the St. Andrews Writers Group. Her work was commended in the competition.

LYS WYNESS is an Aberdonian, writes poetry, short stories, book reviews, articles and books on local history. Publishes, twice yearly, *Wee Gems*, poetry and prose by Bon-Accord Writers. Recently published *Castlegate Characters* through the Aberdeen City Arts Department – Libraries. Is currently working on her next book, *Aberdeen Remembered*. Aims, whenever possible, through her writing, to keep the Buchan language alive. Her work was commended in the competition.